THE **TRUSTED** **LEADER** JOURNAL

Train Your Brain with Daily Practice
to Become a Trusted Leader

A companion to the book *The Trusted Leader:
Use the Partnering Approach to Become
the Trusted Leader People Want to Follow*

SUE **DYER**

 Published by Pendulum Publishing
291 McLeod Street, Livermore CA 94550

Editor: Kevin Anderson and Associates
Cover and journal design by A. Kate Reynolds
Book Launch Director: Amber Vilhauer

ISBN: Journal   978-1-955940-03-0

CONTENTS

ABOUT THE TRUSTED LEADER JOURNAL

Your brain is a beautiful bio-computer where garbage in = garbage out. The brains of most leaders float along with whatever thoughts and feelings are in front of them at any given time. Thoughts are like pebbles in a stream, and you react to what you hit. This kind of "reactionary" approach can be risky for you and your business. As a leader, you need to be able to create an atmosphere of trust, so that your employees, customers, and peers will follow you. To do that, you must get control of your brain so it can work for you, not against you.

"The Trusted Leader Journal" is a companion to my book *The Trusted Leader: Use the Partnering Approach to Become the Trusted Leader People Want to Follow*, in which I lay out the framework for creating a high trust atmosphere for your business. To implement the Partnering Approach framework, the first step is the train your brain to use the Partnering Principles and Values.

TRAIN YOUR BRAIN WITH DAILY PRACTICE

The goal of training your brain incorporates the following:

» **BE ABLE TO CREATE WHAT YOU WANT, NOT WHAT YOU DON'T WANT.**

Most leaders focus on what they don't want or what they are worried about. Your brain thinks you actually WANT what you think about, so it is important to get control of your thoughts so that most of the time, you are thinking about what you do want.

» **MAKE NEURO CONNECTIONS TO YOUR SUBCONSCIOUS SO IT CAN HELP GUIDE YOU.**

The more you can "listen" to your subconscious for guidance, the more you are going to be amazed by what you can create. Most leaders listen to their fight or flight response, which is full of fear. Unless you are about to be eaten by a lion, it is probably not your best source of guidance.

» **ESTABLISH A HIGH TRUST ATMOSPHERE SO YOUR BUSINESS CAN FLOURISH.**

Without a foundation of trust in your business, nothing can happen. You can't lead. Customers and employees won't follow. Even if you are the best and brightest leader ever to walk the earth, you won't be able to lead when your people aren't willing to talk, tell you the truth, collaborate, or innovate. None of these things happen without trust.

» **OVERCOME THE NEGATIVE WORLD WE LIVE IN.**

We are bombarded daily with negative "news." When we send our kids off to school, we tell them to "be careful." We are always hearing about impending doom and as business leaders, we can't help but worry about our business, our employees, and our future. Building an atmosphere with a high level of trust will prove that even in the worst of times, you can thrive. You will learn to trust that this is the case over time, once you drive out fear.

Perfection is not the goal, discipline is. That is why there are six daily practices. No one is going to be perfect. You may have moments of perfection. But the objective is to bring trust, and the discipline of creating trust, to both your conscious and subconscious. Then your actions will always be moving toward creating trust in your business.

PREPARING FOR PRACTICE 1: YOUR MORNING RITUAL

For Practice One, you will need to do some preparation work before you start to train your brain. There are three parts to this prep:

1. Understand how to create a trusting state of mind. This will help you each day to stay in the right frame of mind to achieve your results.
2. Create your Trusted Leader Vision (story). I will walk you through developing this. You will use this every morning.
3. Develop your morning prayer, meditation, or visualization. You can read your vision story or develop another tool to put out the intention you want. I will share with you the morning prayer that I use.

PART 1. Your State of Mind

All martial arts use the concept of *centering* as the key ingredient to successful practice. The philosophy behind this is that if you are centered, then you could balance the entire earth on the head of a pin. So, if you are centered, you can move in all directions with great speed and agility, and achieve success. But how do you get centered? Your morning ritual is what you will use to become centered and grounded for your day. I use two tools to create a state of mind, and I will explain how this works. I will also share with you my morning prayer that I've used for over forty years, so you can see an example of how to use these two tools as part of your own morning ritual.

Your state of mind determines the level of trust you will be able to create. If you don't have the state of mind that you desire, you can adjust it by changing your "vibe." That may sound strange, but everything in the universe vibrates at a specific frequency—particles, atoms, cells, even the earth. If you can vibrate at a higher frequency, you can change your state of mind. Tony Robbins is a master at this. During his seminars, he takes a very large crowd of people and helps them to increase their frequency. Think of listening to a beautiful piece of music. It washes over you and you feel it in your body. What about seeing a great movie or reading a great book? Art can transport you to a new world of new possibilities. When you are in a state of mind that does not serve you, you must learn to change your state.

Let me help you understand what a state of dissonance and a state of harmony feel like so you will be able to detect these in yourself and others. Put on some music. Now start to hum along with the music. Follow the tune and feel how you are *flowing* along with the song. Now, move your humming up a little in tone until you hear your humming *clashing* with the song. Feel your tone bounce against the song's tone—you feel the pulsations of the two waves hitting? Now, take your tone up again until the clashing and pulsing stop. What does it sound like? Harmony. Yes, you are humming a higher note than the song, but they are not clashing because you have found *harmony*. You can learn to detect your state of mind by identifying if your feel harmony or dissonance. You can also do this to see what is happening within your business, your team, or with a customer. With practice, you can walk into a room and take a litmus test on everyones' state of mind—are things clashing or are they in harmony? Clashing likely means entropy (wasted effort).

Every morning, check in on your state of mind. If there is dissonance, work to create harmony. The morning ritual can help you get centered.

PART 2. Your Trusted Leader Vision

You will need to write out a vision for your business to become a high trust, high performing, collaborative, and innovative team. Here is a process to help you: This vision will be your target, to which you are aiming.

A. What would be possible if you led a high trust, collaborative, innovative business? (i.e. 20% more margin, less frustration, increased market share, etc.)

_____

_____

_____

_____

_____

_____

_____

_____

_____

_____

_____

_____

_____

_____

_____

_____

_____

_____

What would this mean ...

TO YOU?

TO YOUR EMPLOYEES?

TO YOUR CUSTOMERS?

TO YOUR VENDORS?

B. Now, write out a vision (story) of your high trust business as if it has already happened. What is it like for you now? How do you feel? What has become possible that was not possible before? Every morning you will read your vision story.

_____

_____

_____

_____

_____

_____

_____

_____

_____

_____

_____

_____

_____

_____

_____

_____

_____

_____

_____

_____

_____

_____

PART 3. Your Morning Prayer or Meditation

The final part of your morning ritual is creating a morning prayer or meditation to get into a great state of mind for your day. This will allow you to set intentions in your subconscious and listen to any messages you receive. Again, it is the practices that will allow you to get better at creating your intentions. To help, I thought I would share with you my morning prayer, so you have an example to use as you develop your own morning prayer/meditation.

As I drive to work each day, I say my morning prayer. I've been saying this prayer every morning of my life for over forty years. I share it with you here, and I will give you some commentary on each section and what it means to me.

SUE'S MORNING PRAYER

> *This is the day that the Lord hath made, I shall rejoice and be glad, for in it all things are made new.*

I grew up in a Christian household, but it does not matter what religion or belief system you have, each day is a new beginning. We let go of the past, of which we have no control. We let go of the future, which is only a promise. We embrace today, the only time where we truly have control. You must try to live in the present. Let every day become a "fresh start" and you will have a wonderous life.

> *The Lord said seek and you shall find, ask and you shall have, knock and the door shall be opened unto you.*
>
> *Act as if you already are the person that you long to be.*

Again, your belief system is your own and should be cherished. This part of my morning prayer focuses on the fact that we create our own day and become the person we decide we will become. We are, at the very least, co-creators of our own life and results, and maybe much more. So, seek, ask and knock—it's okay. "Acting as if" is important to our state of mind. *Acting as if* you already are the person you long to be can be very useful. Dress, act, and feel like you are where you are going, not where you are. This is also about going beyond what you believe you are and considering what God believes you to be. For most of us, our God is too small, and we can't imagine what is possible. I struggle with this every day.

Lord, God, Heavenly Father draw down upon me this day
and grant me your peace, your wisdom, and let your will
be done and not mine. Let me be a vehicle of your love
to all of those that you bring into my life this day.

In this section, I ask to be a partner with God. I say that I am willing to follow, that I give up my will to God's will. This is because ego can get in the way and I want to make sure that ego is not my driving force. Instead, I want to follow God's will—what is good for all; love, kindness, and caring. I also ask that people who come into my life are people to whom I have something to offer. Many times they are a gift to me.

Lord, God, Heavenly Father let this day be glorious,
let it be wonderous—a day filled with INSERT YOUR
DESIRED INTENTION (for example completion, connection,
miracles, movement forward, serenity, joy, etc.)

This section sets up your intention for the day. It leaves the door open for how you might come by these feelings. Each day you can mention specific things you want that day. Sometimes I end this section with, "Today, I expect a miracle." When I do this and truly "expect" one, I am very rarely disappointed. My definition of miracle is something that changes my perspective. It can be a big break-through or overcoming an internal barrier. The size does not matter. Noticing it does.

Lord, God, Heavenly Father is there anything I need to know?

The final section of my morning prayer is about being still and listening. We are trying to connect with our subconscious. See what messages come through. Ask questions like "What do I need to know?" You will know when what pops in your head is true, meaningful, and import-ant. Remember you have neurotransmitters in your gut and heart—so listen with your whole body.

That's it. That's my morning prayer. You will need to develop your own version of a prayer or meditation for your Trusted Leader morning ritual, and you can refer to this section to help you do so. Your belief system is yours and should be celebrated. I offer my prayer as an example in hopes it may be helpful to you.

CREATE YOUR MORNING PRAYER OR MEDITATION

Write out your morning meditation or prayer. You can read it or you can record and play it every morning.

_____

_____

_____

_____

_____

_____

_____

_____

_____

_____

_____

_____

_____

_____

_____

_____

_____

_____

_____

_____

_____

_____

Now you are ready for your daily morning ritual.
You understand your:

- » **PART 1:** State of mind
- » **PART 2:** Vision
- » **PART 3:** Prayer/Meditation

USING THE PARTNERING APPROACH

The partnering approach allows you to think and act like a trusted leader. It is a two-step business paradigm that sets up the intentions (10 Partnering Principles) and the mindset (6 Partnering Values) needed to create a high trust business culture. The intentions help you think like a trusted leader and the mindset values helps to create the behaviors needed in a high trust culture.

In the book, *The Trusted Leader*, refer to chapters five and six for details about the Ten Partnering Principles and Six Partnering Values that make up the Partnering Approach. I've listed the Ten Principles and Six Values below, so you have them as a reference when you are selecting one for your daily intention.

Each day, select one of these 16 principles/values to guide your daily intention.

THE TEN PARTNERING PRINCIPLES = INTENTIONS (HOW YOU THINK)

1. Fear is the enemy of trust
2. Really care
3. People don't argue with what they help to create
4. There is collective wisdom in a team
5. Refuse to be an adversary
6. Set partnering ground rules
7. To improve communication, stop talking and ask good questions
8. Your success is determined by how you react to the challenges you face
9. There is energy in conflict
10. Understand all interests

THE SIX PARTNERING VALUES = CULTURE (HOW YOU ACT)

1. Trust
2. Fairness
3. Transparency
4. Respect
5. Collaboration
6. Helpfulness

GUIDE TO FILLING OUT YOUR
TRUSTED LEADER JOURNAL

The Six Daily Trusted Leader Practices

To train your brain, it is easiest to "stack" new habits together. You will want to do all six of the Trusted Leader Practices each day. They should be incorporated into your routine and not take more than a few minutes at a time. At first you will be highly conscious of doing them, then, over time, they just become just another part of your day.

You will start with a morning ritual of selecting your principle/value and intention. Then you will plan how you will use this throughout your day. Observe and record the insights and reactions you are getting. During your evening ritual, you will note the lessons you've learned, the things you want to do again, those that you will continue to work on, and those you will throw away. You can record your "keepers" at the end of the journal in Your Trusted Leader Arsenal.

You can refer to this section for clarity about what to do for each Daily Practice in your Trusted Leader Journal page.

PRACTICE 1:
Your Morning Ritual

I've outlined your Prep Work for Practice 1 in the section *Preparing for Your Morning Ritual*; check it out so you can:

» Create a high trust state of mind.

» Create Your Ideal Vision of you as the leader of your business. Put emotion into it.

» Create a Meditation or prayer to set your intention for using the Partnering Approach principles and values.

DAILY PRACTICE:

1. Work to create a high trust state of mind for your day.

2. Listen to music and work to create harmony and let go of dissonance.

3. Read your Ideal Vision of you as the leader in your highly successful business.

   • Write down questions or answers that come into your head.

4. Say or listen to a meditation or prayer that allows you to ask for insights and listen to the answers you receive.

   • Put as many emotions into it as you can so you "own" them.

   • Write down what comes to mind.

PRACTICE 2:
Select a Daily Trusted Leader Intention

DAILY PRACTICE:

1. Select ONE Trusted Leader Principle or Value as your focus for the day. Write it in your Trusted Leader Journal. You can go through them in order or pick one that best fits your day.

2. Using your selected principle or value, choose an intention for the day where increased trust will create an extraordinary outcome.

3. If your inner voice is negative, ask your subconscious what to do to achieve this outcome. Write it down in your journal.

PRACTICE 3:
Plan for Using the Trusted Leader Intention Throughout Your Day

DAILY PRACTICE:

1. Review your calendar for the day and plan out how you can incorporate your principle/value into your day. If you need to prepare to achieve a result, then prepare.

2. Write down where/how you plan to use your daily principle or value.

PRACTICE 4:
Observe and Record Responses

DAILY PRACTICE:

1. Throughout the day as you implement your daily intention, observe what happens.

2. Write down what you observe in your journal, noticing other people's reactions and what you think of. You are working to bring what is unconscious into your consciousness.

PRACTICE 5:
Your evening ritual—What did you learn?

DAILY PRACTICE:

1. Write down what you learned today. What happened? What worked? What didn't work? What did you achieve? Did you accomplish your intention?

2. Go to sleep thinking about your intention and how you are on your way to becoming a Trusted Leader!

PRACTICE 6:
Repeat or Tweak?

Do this as part of your evening or morning ritual after you've taken some time to understand your results.

DAILY PRACTICE:

1. Read what you wrote under "lessons learned" in Practice Five.

2. Identify which ones you need to tweak so you get better results. Put a plus sign next to the ones you want to remember to use again.

SAMPLE
PRACTICE
RECORD

DAY**AA** | *5/24/21*

· ·

1 **Your Morning Ritual**

Read/listen to your Trusted Leader Vision.

2 **Your Daily TRUSTED LEADER Intention**

Pick one principle or value.

TODAY'S TL PRINCIPLE/VALUE:

PRINCIPLES
- ☐ Fear is the enemy of trust
- ☑ Really care
- ☐ People don't argue with what they help create
- ☐ There is collective wisdom in a team
- ☐ Refuse to be an adversary
- ☐ Set partnering ground rules
- ☐ To improve communication, stop talking and ask good questions
- ☐ Your success is determined by how you react to the challenges you face
- ☐ There is energy in conflict
- ☐ Understand all interests

VALUES
- ☐ Trust
- ☐ Fairness
- ☐ Transparency
- ☐ Respect
- ☐ Collaboration
- ☐ Helpfuless

MY TL INTENTION TODAY:

Today I will show those that I interact with that I truly care about them.

INNER VOICE FEEDBACK:

Makes me realize I could do this more often I feel guilty for not seeing others more clearly I want to do better

PRACTICE RECORD

3 Plan for Using Your **TRUSTED LEADER** Intention

I WILL INCORPORATE MY INTENTION INTO MY DAY AS FOLLOWS:

Morning Staff meeting - Before and after the meeting I will be specific about the good work people are doing.

Lunch with Bill and Amy - I will tell them how much I appreciate and care about my staff, and about them as key vendors that allow me to succeed.

3pm Project Meeting - Show the project leaders how much I appreciate and care about their efforts. Make sure they have the resources needed to be highly successful.

4pm Personnel Meeting - Make sure I listen to really understand what Jennifer is feeling and why her performance has diminished. Find out what she feels she can do and what she needs. Show her that I care about her and that she is important to me.

7pm Board Meeting - Work to connect with Roger so that I can offer my sincere care and try to overcome the striff that happened last month. Let the Board know how much I appreciate and care about their guidance. Even when it is touogh to hear.

9pm Home - let my kids and spouse know how much they mean to me and that I pick up a small token of my appreciation. Give my spouse a back rub and my kids my time to listen about their day and cares.

Transformation isn't a future event, but a present day activity.
JILLIAN MICHAELS

4 **Observations**

WHAT ARE YOU OBSERVING AS YOU IMPLEMENT YOUR INTENTION?

- *The staff meeting was one of our best. people were more open*

- *Sharing about my care for my staff allowed me great insights*

- *The project team is doing better than expected*

- *Jennifer was open and hones and we figured out a plan forward*

- *I enjoyed the Board meeting more than any one ever*

- *My daughter gave me a big hug and talked to me all night*

-

-

-

-

DAY**AA**

5 Evening Ritual

WHAT DID YOU LEARN TODAY?

⊛ *I felt happier knowing I was going to be more caring*

☐

☐

☐

☐

6 Repeat or Tweak?

Look at your lessons learned, put an "X" next to those that did not work and a "" next to those that did work (and that you want to repeat).*

DAILY
PRACTICE
RECORD

DAY01 | / /

1 Your Morning Ritual
Read/listen to your Trusted Leader Vision.

2 Your Daily TRUSTED LEADER Intention
Pick one principle or value.

TODAY'S TL PRINCIPLE/VALUE:

PRINCIPLES
- [ ] Fear is the enemy of trust
- [ ] Really care
- [ ] People don't argue with what they help create
- [ ] There is collective wisdom in a team
- [ ] Refuse to be an adversary
- [ ] Set partnering ground rules
- [ ] To improve communica- tion, stop talking and ask good questions
- [ ] Your success is determined by how you react to the challenges you face
- [ ] There is energy in conflict
- [ ] Understand all interests

VALUES
- [ ] Trust
- [ ] Fairness
- [ ] Transparency
- [ ] Respect
- [ ] Collaboration
- [ ] Helpfuless

MY TL INTENTION TODAY:

_____

_____

_____

_____

_____

_____

_____

INNER VOICE FEEDBACK:

_____

_____

_____

_____

_____

_____

3 **Plan for Using Your TRUSTED LEADER Intention**

I WILL INCORPORATE MY INTENTION INTO MY DAY AS FOLLOWS:

Life is an experiment.
RALPH WALDO EMERSON

④ Observations

WHAT ARE YOU OBSERVING AS YOU IMPLEMENT YOUR INTENTION?

-

-

-

-

-

-

-

-

-

-

5 **Evening Ritual**

WHAT DID YOU LEARN TODAY?

☐

☐

☐

☐

☐

6 **Repeat or Tweak?**
Look at your lessons learned, put an "X" next to those that did not work and a "*" next to those that did work (and that you want to repeat).

DAY02 | / /

① Your Morning Ritual

Read/listen to your Trusted Leader Vision.

② Your Daily TRUSTED LEADER Intention

Pick one principle or value.

TODAY'S TL PRINCIPLE/VALUE:

PRINCIPLES

- ☐ Fear is the enemy of trust
- ☐ Really care
- ☐ People don't argue with what they help create
- ☐ There is collective wisdom in a team
- ☐ Refuse to be an adversary
- ☐ Set partnering ground rules
- ☐ To improve communication, stop talking and ask good questions
- ☐ Your success is determined by how you react to the challenges you face
- ☐ There is energy in conflict
- ☐ Understand all interests

VALUES

- ☐ Trust
- ☐ Fairness
- ☐ Transparency
- ☐ Respect
- ☐ Collaboration
- ☐ Helpfuless

MY TL INTENTION TODAY:

_____

_____

_____

_____

_____

_____

_____

_____

INNER VOICE FEEDBACK:

_____

_____

_____

_____

_____

_____

_____

. . . .

3 Plan for Using Your **TRUSTED LEADER** Intention

I WILL INCORPORATE MY INTENTION INTO MY DAY AS FOLLOWS:

Life is an experiment.
RALPH WALDO EMERSON

4 Observations

WHAT ARE YOU OBSERVING AS YOU IMPLEMENT YOUR INTENTION?

-
-
-
-
-
-
-
-
-
-

5 **Evening Ritual**

WHAT DID YOU LEARN TODAY?

- ☐
- ☐
- ☐
- ☐
- ☐

6 **Repeat or Tweak?**

Look at your lessons learned, put an "X" next to those that did not work and a "" next to those that did work (and that you want to repeat).*

DAY03 | / /

1 Your Morning Ritual
Read/listen to your Trusted Leader Vision.

2 Your Daily TRUSTED LEADER Intention
Pick one principle or value.

TODAY'S TL PRINCIPLE/VALUE:

PRINCIPLES
- ☐ Fear is the enemy of trust
- ☐ Really care
- ☐ People don't argue with what they help create
- ☐ There is collective wisdom in a team
- ☐ Refuse to be an adversary
- ☐ Set partnering ground rules
- ☐ To improve communication, stop talking and ask good questions
- ☐ Your success is determined by how you react to the challenges you face
- ☐ There is energy in conflict
- ☐ Understand all interests

VALUES
- ☐ Trust
- ☐ Fairness
- ☐ Transparency
- ☐ Respect
- ☐ Collaboration
- ☐ Helpfuless

MY TL INTENTION TODAY:

INNER VOICE FEEDBACK:

3 Plan for Using Your **TRUSTED LEADER** Intention

I WILL INCORPORATE MY INTENTION INTO MY DAY AS FOLLOWS:

Life is an experiment.
RALPH WALDO EMERSON

4 **Observations**

WHAT ARE YOU OBSERVING AS YOU IMPLEMENT YOUR INTENTION?

-

-

-

-

-

-

-

-

-

-

5 Evening Ritual

WHAT DID YOU LEARN TODAY?

☐

☐

☐

☐

☐

6 Repeat or Tweak?

Look at your lessons learned, put an "X" next to those that did not work and a "*" next to those that did work (and that you want to repeat).

DAY04 | / /

1 **Your Morning Ritual**

Read/listen to your Trusted Leader Vision.

2 **Your Daily TRUSTED LEADER Intention**

Pick one principle or value.

TODAY'S TL PRINCIPLE/VALUE:

PRINCIPLES

- ☐ Fear is the enemy of trust
- ☐ Really care
- ☐ People don't argue with what they help create
- ☐ There is collective wisdom in a team
- ☐ Refuse to be an adversary
- ☐ Set partnering ground rules
- ☐ To improve communica-tion, stop talking and ask good questions
- ☐ Your success is determined by how you react to the challenges you face
- ☐ There is energy in conflict
- ☐ Understand all interests

VALUES

- ☐ Trust
- ☐ Fairness
- ☐ Transparency
- ☐ Respect
- ☐ Collaboration
- ☐ Helpfuless

MY TL INTENTION TODAY:

_____

_____

_____

_____

_____

_____

_____

_____

INNER VOICE FEEDBACK:

_____

_____

_____

_____

_____

_____

_____

_____

3 Plan for Using Your TRUSTED LEADER Intention

I WILL INCORPORATE MY INTENTION INTO MY DAY AS FOLLOWS:

_____

_____

_____

_____

_____

_____

_____

_____

_____

_____

_____

_____

_____

_____

_____

_____

_____

_____

_____

_____

_____

_____

Life is an experiment.
RALPH WALDO EMERSON

4 Observations

WHAT ARE YOU OBSERVING AS YOU IMPLEMENT YOUR INTENTION?

-

-

-

-

-

-

-

-

-

-

5 Evening Ritual

WHAT DID YOU LEARN TODAY?

☐

☐

☐

☐

☐

6 Repeat or Tweak?

Look at your lessons learned, put an "X" next to those that did not work and a "*" next to those that did work (and that you want to repeat).

DAY05 | / /

1 Your Morning Ritual
Read/listen to your Trusted Leader Vision.

2 Your Daily TRUSTED LEADER Intention
Pick one principle or value.

TODAY'S TL PRINCIPLE/VALUE:

MY TL INTENTION TODAY:

PRINCIPLES

- ☐ Fear is the enemy of trust
- ☐ Really care
- ☐ People don't argue with what they help create
- ☐ There is collective wisdom in a team
- ☐ Refuse to be an adversary
- ☐ Set partnering ground rules
- ☐ To improve communica-tion, stop talking and ask good questions
- ☐ Your success is determined by how you react to the challenges you face
- ☐ There is energy in conflict
- ☐ Understand all interests

VALUES

- ☐ Trust
- ☐ Fairness
- ☐ Transparency
- ☐ Respect
- ☐ Collaboration
- ☐ Helpfuless

INNER VOICE FEEDBACK:

3 Plan for Using Your TRUSTED LEADER Intention

I WILL INCORPORATE MY INTENTION INTO MY DAY AS FOLLOWS:

4 Observations

WHAT ARE YOU OBSERVING AS YOU IMPLEMENT YOUR INTENTION?

-
-
-
-
-
-
-
-
-
-

5 Evening Ritual

WHAT DID YOU LEARN TODAY?

☐

☐

☐

☐

☐

6 Repeat or Tweak?

Look at your lessons learned, put an "X" next to those that did not work and a "*" next to those that did work (and that you want to repeat).

WEEKLY **INSIGHTS**

1 This Week's Insights

_____

_____

_____

_____

_____

_____

_____

_____

2 This Week's Lessons Learned

_____

_____

_____

_____

_____

_____

_____

_____

3 Things to Add to My Trusted Leader Arsenal

_____

_____

_____

_____

_____

_____

_____

Notes

DAY06 | / /

1 Your Morning Ritual
Read/listen to your Trusted Leader Vision.

2 Your Daily TRUSTED LEADER Intention
Pick one principle or value.

TODAY'S TL PRINCIPLE/VALUE:

PRINCIPLES
- ☐ Fear is the enemy of trust
- ☐ Really care
- ☐ People don't argue with what they help create
- ☐ There is collective wisdom in a team
- ☐ Refuse to be an adversary
- ☐ Set partnering ground rules
- ☐ To improve communication, stop talking and ask good questions
- ☐ Your success is determined by how you react to the challenges you face
- ☐ There is energy in conflict
- ☐ Understand all interests

VALUES
- ☐ Trust
- ☐ Fairness
- ☐ Transparency
- ☐ Respect
- ☐ Collaboration
- ☐ Helpfuless

MY TL INTENTION TODAY:

INNER VOICE FEEDBACK:

3 **Plan for Using Your TRUSTED LEADER Intention**

I WILL INCORPORATE MY INTENTION INTO MY DAY AS FOLLOWS:

He who does not trust enough will NOT be trusted.
LAO TZU

. . . .

4 **Observations**

WHAT ARE YOU OBSERVING AS YOU IMPLEMENT YOUR INTENTION?

-

-

-

-

-

-

-

-

-

-

5 Evening Ritual

WHAT DID YOU LEARN TODAY?

☐

☐

☐

☐

☐

6 Repeat or Tweak?

Look at your lessons learned, put an "X" next to those that did not work and a "" next to those that did work (and that you want to repeat).*

DAY07 | / /

1 Your Morning Ritual
Read/listen to your Trusted Leader Vision.

2 Your Daily TRUSTED LEADER Intention
Pick one principle or value.

TODAY'S TL PRINCIPLE/VALUE:

PRINCIPLES

- ☐ Fear is the enemy of trust
- ☐ Really care
- ☐ People don't argue with what they help create
- ☐ There is collective wisdom in a team
- ☐ Refuse to be an adversary
- ☐ Set partnering ground rules
- ☐ To improve communication, stop talking and ask good questions
- ☐ Your success is determined by how you react to the challenges you face
- ☐ There is energy in conflict
- ☐ Understand all interests

VALUES

- ☐ Trust
- ☐ Fairness
- ☐ Transparency
- ☐ Respect
- ☐ Collaboration
- ☐ Helpfuless

MY TL INTENTION TODAY:

INNER VOICE FEEDBACK:

3 **Plan for Using Your TRUSTED LEADER Intention**

I WILL INCORPORATE MY INTENTION INTO MY DAY AS FOLLOWS:

He who does not trust enough will NOT be trusted.
LAO TZU

....

4 **Observations**

WHAT ARE YOU OBSERVING AS YOU IMPLEMENT YOUR INTENTION?

-

-

-

-

-

-

-

-

-

-

5 **Evening Ritual**

WHAT DID YOU LEARN TODAY?

- [ ]
- [ ]
- [ ]
- [ ]
- [ ]

6 **Repeat or Tweak?**

Look at your lessons learned, put an "X" next to those that did not work and a "" next to those that did work (and that you want to repeat).*

DAY08 | / /

1 Your Morning Ritual
Read/listen to your Trusted Leader Vision.

2 Your Daily TRUSTED LEADER Intention
Pick one principle or value.

TODAY'S TL PRINCIPLE/VALUE:

PRINCIPLES
- ☐ Fear is the enemy of trust
- ☐ Really care
- ☐ People don't argue with what they help create
- ☐ There is collective wisdom in a team
- ☐ Refuse to be an adversary
- ☐ Set partnering ground rules
- ☐ To improve communication, stop talking and ask good questions
- ☐ Your success is determined by how you react to the challenges you face
- ☐ There is energy in conflict
- ☐ Understand all interests

VALUES
- ☐ Trust
- ☐ Fairness
- ☐ Transparency
- ☐ Respect
- ☐ Collaboration
- ☐ Helpfuless

MY TL INTENTION TODAY:

INNER VOICE FEEDBACK:

3 Plan for Using Your **TRUSTED LEADER** Intention

I WILL INCORPORATE MY INTENTION INTO MY DAY AS FOLLOWS:

_____

_____

_____

_____

_____

_____

_____

_____

_____

_____

_____

_____

_____

_____

_____

_____

_____

_____

_____

_____

He who does not trust enough will NOT be trusted.
  LAO TZU

. . . .

4 **Observations**

WHAT ARE YOU OBSERVING AS YOU IMPLEMENT YOUR INTENTION?

-
-
-
-
-
-
-
-
-
-

5 Evening Ritual

WHAT DID YOU LEARN TODAY?

☐

☐

☐

☐

☐

6 Repeat or Tweak?

Look at your lessons learned, put an "X" next to those that did not work and a "" next to those that did work (and that you want to repeat).*

DAY09 | / /

1 Your Morning Ritual
Read/listen to your Trusted Leader Vision.

2 Your Daily TRUSTED LEADER Intention
Pick one principle or value.

TODAY'S TL PRINCIPLE/VALUE:

MY TL INTENTION TODAY:

PRINCIPLES
- ☐ Fear is the enemy of trust
- ☐ Really care
- ☐ People don't argue with what they help create
- ☐ There is collective wisdom in a team
- ☐ Refuse to be an adversary
- ☐ Set partnering ground rules
- ☐ To improve communication, stop talking and ask good questions
- ☐ Your success is determined by how you react to the challenges you face
- ☐ There is energy in conflict
- ☐ Understand all interests

VALUES
- ☐ Trust
- ☐ Fairness
- ☐ Transparency
- ☐ Respect
- ☐ Collaboration
- ☐ Helpfuless

INNER VOICE FEEDBACK:

3 **Plan for Using Your TRUSTED LEADER Intention**

I WILL INCORPORATE MY INTENTION INTO MY DAY AS FOLLOWS:

He who does not trust enough will NOT be trusted.
LAO TZU

. . . .

4 **Observations**

WHAT ARE YOU OBSERVING AS YOU IMPLEMENT YOUR INTENTION?

-
-
-
-
-
-
-
-
-
-

5 **Evening Ritual**

WHAT DID YOU LEARN TODAY?

☐

☐

☐

☐

☐

6 **Repeat or Tweak?**
Look at your lessons learned, put an "X" next to those that did not work and a "*" next to those that did work (and that you want to repeat).

DAY10 | / /

1 Your Morning Ritual
Read/listen to your Trusted Leader Vision.

2 Your Daily TRUSTED LEADER Intention
Pick one principle or value.

TODAY'S TL PRINCIPLE/VALUE:

PRINCIPLES
- ☐ Fear is the enemy of trust
- ☐ Really care
- ☐ People don't argue with what they help create
- ☐ There is collective wisdom in a team
- ☐ Refuse to be an adversary
- ☐ Set partnering ground rules
- ☐ To improve communica-tion, stop talking and ask good questions
- ☐ Your success is determined by how you react to the challenges you face
- ☐ There is energy in conflict
- ☐ Understand all interests

VALUES
- ☐ Trust
- ☐ Fairness
- ☐ Transparency
- ☐ Respect
- ☐ Collaboration
- ☐ Helpfuless

MY TL INTENTION TODAY:

INNER VOICE FEEDBACK:

3 **Plan for Using Your TRUSTED LEADER Intention**

I WILL INCORPORATE MY INTENTION INTO MY DAY AS FOLLOWS:

He who does not trust enough will NOT be trusted.
LAO TZU

· ·

4 Observations

WHAT ARE YOU OBSERVING AS YOU IMPLEMENT YOUR INTENTION?

-
-
-
-
-
-
-
-
-
-

5 Evening Ritual

WHAT DID YOU LEARN TODAY?

☐ _____

☐ _____

☐ _____

☐ _____

☐ _____

6 Repeat or Tweak?

Look at your lessons learned, put an "X" next to those that did not work and a "*" next to those that did work (and that you want to repeat).

WEEKLY INSIGHTS

1 This Week's Insights

_____
_____
_____
_____
_____
_____
_____

2 This Week's Lessons Learned

_____
_____
_____
_____
_____
_____
_____

3 Things to Add to My Trusted Leader Arsenal

_____
_____
_____
_____
_____
_____

Notes

DAY 11 | / /

1 **Your Morning Ritual**

Read/listen to your Trusted Leader Vision.

2 **Your Daily TRUSTED LEADER Intention**

Pick one principle or value.

TODAY'S TL PRINCIPLE/VALUE:

PRINCIPLES

- ☐ Fear is the enemy of trust
- ☐ Really care
- ☐ People don't argue with what they help create
- ☐ There is collective wisdom in a team
- ☐ Refuse to be an adversary
- ☐ Set partnering ground rules
- ☐ To improve communication, stop talking and ask good questions
- ☐ Your success is determined by how you react to the challenges you face
- ☐ There is energy in conflict
- ☐ Understand all interests

VALUES

- ☐ Trust
- ☐ Fairness
- ☐ Transparency
- ☐ Respect
- ☐ Collaboration
- ☐ Helpfuless

MY TL INTENTION TODAY:

INNER VOICE FEEDBACK:

3 **Plan for Using Your TRUSTED LEADER Intention**

I WILL INCORPORATE MY INTENTION INTO MY DAY AS FOLLOWS:

Trust starts with trustworthy leadership. It must be built into the corporate culture.
RALPH WALDO EMERSON

· ·

4 Observations

WHAT ARE YOU OBSERVING AS YOU IMPLEMENT YOUR INTENTION?

-
-
-
-
-
-
-
-
-
-

5 **Evening Ritual**

WHAT DID YOU LEARN TODAY?

☐

☐

☐

☐

☐

6 **Repeat or Tweak?**

Look at your lessons learned, put an "X" next to those that did not work and a "*" next to those that did work (and that you want to repeat).

DAY12 | / /

① Your Morning Ritual
Read/listen to your Trusted Leader Vision.

② Your Daily TRUSTED LEADER Intention
Pick one principle or value.

TODAY'S TL PRINCIPLE/VALUE:

PRINCIPLES
- ☐ Fear is the enemy of trust
- ☐ Really care
- ☐ People don't argue with what they help create
- ☐ There is collective wisdom in a team
- ☐ Refuse to be an adversary
- ☐ Set partnering ground rules
- ☐ To improve communica-tion, stop talking and ask good questions
- ☐ Your success is determined by how you react to the challenges you face
- ☐ There is energy in conflict
- ☐ Understand all interests

VALUES
- ☐ Trust
- ☐ Fairness
- ☐ Transparency
- ☐ Respect
- ☐ Collaboration
- ☐ Helpfuless

MY TL INTENTION TODAY:

_____

_____

_____

_____

_____

_____

_____

INNER VOICE FEEDBACK:

_____

_____

_____

_____

_____

_____

_____

3 Plan for Using Your TRUSTED LEADER Intention

I WILL INCORPORATE MY INTENTION INTO MY DAY AS FOLLOWS:

Trust starts with trustworthy leadership. It must be built into the corporate culture.
RALPH WALDO EMERSON

④ Observations

WHAT ARE YOU OBSERVING AS YOU IMPLEMENT YOUR INTENTION?

-
-
-
-
-
-
-
-
-
-

5 **Evening Ritual**

WHAT DID YOU LEARN TODAY?

☐

☐

☐

☐

☐

6 **Repeat or Tweak?**

Look at your lessons learned, put an "X" next to those that did not work and a "" next to those that did work (and that you want to repeat).*

DAY13 | / /

1 Your Morning Ritual
Read/listen to your Trusted Leader Vision.

2 Your Daily TRUSTED LEADER Intention
Pick one principle or value.

TODAY'S TL PRINCIPLE/VALUE:

PRINCIPLES
- ☐ Fear is the enemy of trust
- ☐ Really care
- ☐ People don't argue with what they help create
- ☐ There is collective wisdom in a team
- ☐ Refuse to be an adversary
- ☐ Set partnering ground rules
- ☐ To improve communica-tion, stop talking and ask good questions
- ☐ Your success is determined by how you react to the challenges you face
- ☐ There is energy in conflict
- ☐ Understand all interests

VALUES
- ☐ Trust
- ☐ Fairness
- ☐ Transparency
- ☐ Respect
- ☐ Collaboration
- ☐ Helpfuless

MY TL INTENTION TODAY:

INNER VOICE FEEDBACK:

3 Plan for Using Your TRUSTED LEADER Intention

I WILL INCORPORATE MY INTENTION INTO MY DAY AS FOLLOWS:

Trust starts with trustworthy leadership. It must be built into the corporate culture.
RALPH WALDO EMERSON

4 **Observations**

WHAT ARE YOU OBSERVING AS YOU IMPLEMENT YOUR INTENTION?

-
-
-
-
-
-
-
-
-
-

5 **Evening Ritual**

WHAT DID YOU LEARN TODAY?

☐

☐

☐

☐

☐

6 **Repeat or Tweak?**

Look at your lessons learned, put an "X" next to those that did not work and a "" next to those that did work (and that you want to repeat).*

DAY14 | / /

1 **Your Morning Ritual**

Read/listen to your Trusted Leader Vision.

2 **Your Daily TRUSTED LEADER Intention**

Pick one principle or value.

TODAY'S TL PRINCIPLE/VALUE:

PRINCIPLES

☐ Fear is the enemy of trust

☐ Really care

☐ People don't argue with what they help create

☐ There is collective wisdom in a team

☐ Refuse to be an adversary

☐ Set partnering ground rules

☐ To improve communication, stop talking and ask good questions

☐ Your success is determined by how you react to the challenges you face

☐ There is energy in conflict

☐ Understand all interests

VALUES

☐ Trust

☐ Fairness

☐ Transparency

☐ Respect

☐ Collaboration

☐ Helpfuless

MY TL INTENTION TODAY:

_____

_____

_____

_____

_____

_____

_____

_____

INNER VOICE FEEDBACK:

_____

_____

_____

_____

_____

_____

_____

3 **Plan for Using Your TRUSTED LEADER Intention**

I WILL INCORPORATE MY INTENTION INTO MY DAY AS FOLLOWS:

Trust starts with trustworthy leadership. It must be built into the corporate culture.
RALPH WALDO EMERSON

4 Observations

WHAT ARE YOU OBSERVING AS YOU IMPLEMENT YOUR INTENTION?

-
-
-
-
-
-
-
-
-
-

5 Evening Ritual

WHAT DID YOU LEARN TODAY?

☐ _____

☐ _____

☐ _____

☐ _____

☐ _____

6 Repeat or Tweak?

Look at your lessons learned, put an "X" next to those that did not work and a "*" next to those that did work (and that you want to repeat).

DAY 15 | / /

1 Your Morning Ritual
Read/listen to your Trusted Leader Vision.

2 Your Daily TRUSTED LEADER Intention
Pick one principle or value.

TODAY'S TL PRINCIPLE/VALUE:

PRINCIPLES
- ☐ Fear is the enemy of trust
- ☐ Really care
- ☐ People don't argue with what they help create
- ☐ There is collective wisdom in a team
- ☐ Refuse to be an adversary
- ☐ Set partnering ground rules
- ☐ To improve communication, stop talking and ask good questions
- ☐ Your success is determined by how you react to the challenges you face
- ☐ There is energy in conflict
- ☐ Understand all interests

VALUES
- ☐ Trust
- ☐ Fairness
- ☐ Transparency
- ☐ Respect
- ☐ Collaboration
- ☐ Helpfuless

MY TL INTENTION TODAY:

INNER VOICE FEEDBACK:

3 Plan for Using Your **TRUSTED LEADER** Intention

I WILL INCORPORATE MY INTENTION INTO MY DAY AS FOLLOWS:

Trust starts with trustworthy leadership. It must be built into the corporate culture.
RALPH WALDO EMERSON

. . . .

4 **Observations**

WHAT ARE YOU OBSERVING AS YOU IMPLEMENT YOUR INTENTION?

-
-
-
-
-
-
-
-
-
-

5 Evening Ritual

WHAT DID YOU LEARN TODAY?

☐

☐

☐

☐

☐

6 Repeat or Tweak?

Look at your lessons learned, put an "X" next to those that did not work and a "" next to those that did work (and that you want to repeat).*

WEEKLY INSIGHTS

1 This Week's Insights

_____
_____
_____
_____
_____
_____
_____
_____

2 This Week's Lessons Learned

_____
_____
_____
_____
_____
_____
_____

3 Things to Add to My Trusted Leader Arsenal

_____
_____
_____
_____
_____
_____

Notes

DAY16 | / /

① Your Morning Ritual
Read/listen to your Trusted Leader Vision.

② Your Daily TRUSTED LEADER Intention
Pick one principle or value.

TODAY'S TL PRINCIPLE/VALUE:

PRINCIPLES
- ☐ Fear is the enemy of trust
- ☐ Really care
- ☐ People don't argue with what they help create
- ☐ There is collective wisdom in a team
- ☐ Refuse to be an adversary
- ☐ Set partnering ground rules
- ☐ To improve communication, stop talking and ask good questions
- ☐ Your success is determined by how you react to the challenges you face
- ☐ There is energy in conflict
- ☐ Understand all interests

VALUES
- ☐ Trust
- ☐ Fairness
- ☐ Transparency
- ☐ Respect
- ☐ Collaboration
- ☐ Helpfuless

MY TL INTENTION TODAY:

_____

_____

_____

_____

_____

_____

_____

INNER VOICE FEEDBACK:

_____

_____

_____

_____

_____

_____

_____

3 Plan for Using Your **TRUSTED LEADER** Intention

I WILL INCORPORATE MY INTENTION INTO MY DAY AS FOLLOWS:

WEEK 4

4 Observations

WHAT ARE YOU OBSERVING AS YOU IMPLEMENT YOUR INTENTION?

-
-
-
-
-
-
-
-
-
-

5 Evening Ritual

WHAT DID YOU LEARN TODAY?

☐ _____

☐ _____

☐ _____

☐ _____

☐ _____

6 Repeat or Tweak?

Look at your lessons learned, put an "X" next to those that did not work and a "*" next to those that did work (and that you want to repeat).

DAY17 | / /

· ·

1 **Your Morning Ritual**

Read/listen to your Trusted Leader Vision.

2 **Your Daily TRUSTED LEADER Intention**

Pick one principle or value.

TODAY'S TL PRINCIPLE/VALUE:

PRINCIPLES	VALUES
☐ Fear is the enemy of trust	☐ Trust
☐ Really care	☐ Fairness
☐ People don't argue with what they help create	☐ Transparency
	☐ Respect
☐ There is collective wisdom in a team	☐ Collaboration
☐ Refuse to be an adversary	☐ Helpfuless
☐ Set partnering ground rules	
☐ To improve communica- tion, stop talking and ask good questions	
☐ Your success is determined by how you react to the challenges you face	
☐ There is energy in conflict	
☐ Understand all interests	

MY TL INTENTION TODAY:

_____

_____

_____

_____

_____

_____

_____

_____

INNER VOICE FEEDBACK:

_____

_____

_____

_____

_____

_____

_____

3 **Plan for Using Your TRUSTED LEADER Intention**

I WILL INCORPORATE MY INTENTION INTO MY DAY AS FOLLOWS:

Success is predictable.
BRIAN TRACY

· ·

4 Observations

WHAT ARE YOU OBSERVING AS YOU IMPLEMENT YOUR INTENTION?

-
-
-
-
-
-
-
-
-
-

5 Evening Ritual

WHAT DID YOU LEARN TODAY?

☐

☐

☐

☐

☐

6 Repeat or Tweak?

Look at your lessons learned, put an "X" next to those that did not work and a "" next to those that did work (and that you want to repeat).*

DAY**18** | / /

1 Your Morning Ritual
Read/listen to your Trusted Leader Vision.

2 Your Daily **TRUSTED LEADER** Intention
Pick one principle or value.

TODAY'S TL PRINCIPLE/VALUE:

PRINCIPLES
- [ ] Fear is the enemy of trust
- [ ] Really care
- [ ] People don't argue with what they help create
- [ ] There is collective wisdom in a team
- [ ] Refuse to be an adversary
- [ ] Set partnering ground rules
- [ ] To improve communication, stop talking and ask good questions
- [ ] Your success is determined by how you react to the challenges you face
- [ ] There is energy in conflict
- [ ] Understand all interests

VALUES
- [ ] Trust
- [ ] Fairness
- [ ] Transparency
- [ ] Respect
- [ ] Collaboration
- [ ] Helpfuless

MY TL INTENTION TODAY:

_____

_____

_____

_____

_____

_____

_____

_____

INNER VOICE FEEDBACK:

_____

_____

_____

_____

_____

_____

_____

3 Plan for Using Your **TRUSTED LEADER** Intention

I WILL INCORPORATE MY INTENTION INTO MY DAY AS FOLLOWS:

4 Observations

WHAT ARE YOU OBSERVING AS YOU IMPLEMENT YOUR INTENTION?

-
-
-
-
-
-
-
-
-
-

5 Evening Ritual

WHAT DID YOU LEARN TODAY?

☐

☐

☐

☐

☐

6 Repeat or Tweak?

Look at your lessons learned, put an "X" next to those that did not work and a "" next to those that did work (and that you want to repeat).*

DAY19 | / /

1 Your Morning Ritual
Read/listen to your Trusted Leader Vision.

2 Your Daily TRUSTED LEADER Intention
Pick one principle or value.

TODAY'S TL PRINCIPLE/VALUE:

PRINCIPLES
- ☐ Fear is the enemy of trust
- ☐ Really care
- ☐ People don't argue with what they help create
- ☐ There is collective wisdom in a team
- ☐ Refuse to be an adversary
- ☐ Set partnering ground rules
- ☐ To improve communication, stop talking and ask good questions
- ☐ Your success is determined by how you react to the challenges you face
- ☐ There is energy in conflict
- ☐ Understand all interests

VALUES
- ☐ Trust
- ☐ Fairness
- ☐ Transparency
- ☐ Respect
- ☐ Collaboration
- ☐ Helpfuless

MY TL INTENTION TODAY:

_____

_____

_____

_____

_____

_____

_____

_____

INNER VOICE FEEDBACK:

_____

_____

_____

_____

_____

_____

_____

_____

3 **Plan for Using Your TRUSTED LEADER Intention**

I WILL INCORPORATE MY INTENTION INTO MY DAY AS FOLLOWS:

4 Observations

WHAT ARE YOU OBSERVING AS YOU IMPLEMENT YOUR INTENTION?

-

-

-

-

-

-

-

-

-

-

5 Evening Ritual

WHAT DID YOU LEARN TODAY?

☐

☐

☐

☐

☐

6 Repeat or Tweak?

Look at your lessons learned, put an "X" next to those that did not work and a "" next to those that did work (and that you want to repeat).*

DAY20 | / /

1 **Your Morning Ritual**

Read/listen to your Trusted Leader Vision.

2 **Your Daily TRUSTED LEADER Intention**

Pick one principle or value.

TODAY'S TL PRINCIPLE/VALUE:

PRINCIPLES

- ☐ Fear is the enemy of trust
- ☐ Really care
- ☐ People don't argue with what they help create
- ☐ There is collective wisdom in a team
- ☐ Refuse to be an adversary
- ☐ Set partnering ground rules
- ☐ To improve communica-tion, stop talking and ask good questions
- ☐ Your success is determined by how you react to the challenges you face
- ☐ There is energy in conflict
- ☐ Understand all interests

VALUES

- ☐ Trust
- ☐ Fairness
- ☐ Transparency
- ☐ Respect
- ☐ Collaboration
- ☐ Helpfuless

MY TL INTENTION TODAY:

_____

_____

_____

_____

_____

_____

_____

_____

INNER VOICE FEEDBACK:

_____

_____

_____

_____

_____

_____

_____

3 Plan for Using Your **TRUSTED LEADER** Intention

I WILL INCORPORATE MY INTENTION INTO MY DAY AS FOLLOWS:

- -

4 **Observations**

WHAT ARE YOU OBSERVING AS YOU IMPLEMENT YOUR INTENTION?

-

-

-

-

-

-

-

-

-

-

5 **Evening Ritual**

WHAT DID YOU LEARN TODAY?

☐

☐

☐

☐

☐

6 **Repeat or Tweak?**

Look at your lessons learned, put an "X" next to those that did not work and a "*" next to those that did work (and that you want to repeat).

WEEKLY INSIGHTS

1 This Week's Insights

_____
_____
_____
_____
_____
_____
_____
_____

2 This Week's Lessons Learned

_____
_____
_____
_____
_____
_____
_____
_____

3 Things to Add to My Trusted Leader Arsenal

_____
_____
_____
_____
_____
_____
_____

Notes

DAY21 | / /

1 **Your Morning Ritual**
Read/listen to your Trusted Leader Vision.

2 **Your Daily TRUSTED LEADER Intention**
Pick one principle or value.

TODAY'S TL PRINCIPLE/VALUE:

PRINCIPLES
- ☐ Fear is the enemy of trust
- ☐ Really care
- ☐ People don't argue with what they help create
- ☐ There is collective wisdom in a team
- ☐ Refuse to be an adversary
- ☐ Set partnering ground rules
- ☐ To improve communica- tion, stop talking and ask good questions
- ☐ Your success is determined by how you react to the challenges you face
- ☐ There is energy in conflict
- ☐ Understand all interests

VALUES
- ☐ Trust
- ☐ Fairness
- ☐ Transparency
- ☐ Respect
- ☐ Collaboration
- ☐ Helpfuless

MY TL INTENTION TODAY:

_____

_____

_____

_____

_____

_____

_____

_____

INNER VOICE FEEDBACK:

_____

_____

_____

_____

_____

_____

_____

3 Plan for Using Your TRUSTED LEADER Intention

I WILL INCORPORATE MY INTENTION INTO MY DAY AS FOLLOWS:

4 **Observations**

WHAT ARE YOU OBSERVING AS YOU IMPLEMENT YOUR INTENTION?

-
-
-
-
-
-
-
-
-
-

5 **Evening Ritual**

WHAT DID YOU LEARN TODAY?

☐

☐

☐

☐

☐

6 **Repeat or Tweak?**

Look at your lessons learned, put an "X" next to those that did not work and a "" next to those that did work (and that you want to repeat).*

DAY22 | / /

1 **Your Morning Ritual**

Read/listen to your Trusted Leader Vision.

2 **Your Daily TRUSTED LEADER Intention**

Pick one principle or value.

TODAY'S TL PRINCIPLE/VALUE:

PRINCIPLES

- ☐ Fear is the enemy of trust
- ☐ Really care
- ☐ People don't argue with what they help create
- ☐ There is collective wisdom in a team
- ☐ Refuse to be an adversary
- ☐ Set partnering ground rules
- ☐ To improve communica- tion, stop talking and ask good questions
- ☐ Your success is determined by how you react to the challenges you face
- ☐ There is energy in conflict
- ☐ Understand all interests

VALUES

- ☐ Trust
- ☐ Fairness
- ☐ Transparency
- ☐ Respect
- ☐ Collaboration
- ☐ Helpfuless

MY TL INTENTION TODAY:

_____

_____

_____

_____

_____

_____

_____

_____

INNER VOICE FEEDBACK:

_____

_____

_____

_____

_____

_____

3 **Plan for Using Your TRUSTED LEADER Intention**

I WILL INCORPORATE MY INTENTION INTO MY DAY AS FOLLOWS:

4 Observations

WHAT ARE YOU OBSERVING AS YOU IMPLEMENT YOUR INTENTION?

-

-

-

-

-

-

-

-

-

-

5 Evening Ritual

WHAT DID YOU LEARN TODAY?

☐

☐

☐

☐

☐

6 Repeat or Tweak?

Look at your lessons learned, put an "X" next to those that did not work and a "" next to those that did work (and that you want to repeat).*

DAY23 | / /

1 Your Morning Ritual

Read/listen to your Trusted Leader Vision.

2 Your Daily TRUSTED LEADER Intention

Pick one principle or value.

TODAY'S TL PRINCIPLE/VALUE:

PRINCIPLES
- ☐ Fear is the enemy of trust
- ☐ Really care
- ☐ People don't argue with what they help create
- ☐ There is collective wisdom in a team
- ☐ Refuse to be an adversary
- ☐ Set partnering ground rules
- ☐ To improve communica-tion, stop talking and ask good questions
- ☐ Your success is determined by how you react to the challenges you face
- ☐ There is energy in conflict
- ☐ Understand all interests

VALUES
- ☐ Trust
- ☐ Fairness
- ☐ Transparency
- ☐ Respect
- ☐ Collaboration
- ☐ Helpfuless

MY TL INTENTION TODAY:

_____

_____

_____

_____

_____

_____

_____

INNER VOICE FEEDBACK:

_____

_____

_____

_____

_____

_____

_____

③ Plan for Using Your TRUSTED LEADER Intention

I WILL INCORPORATE MY INTENTION INTO MY DAY AS FOLLOWS:

4 Observations

WHAT ARE YOU OBSERVING AS YOU IMPLEMENT YOUR INTENTION?

-

-

-

-

-

-

-

-

-

-

DAY**23**

5 Evening Ritual

WHAT DID YOU LEARN TODAY?

☐

☐

☐

☐

☐

WEEK 5

6 Repeat or Tweak?

Look at your lessons learned, put an "X" next to those that did not work and a "*" next to those that did work (and that you want to repeat).

DAY24 | / /

① Your Morning Ritual

Read/listen to your Trusted Leader Vision.

② Your Daily TRUSTED LEADER Intention

Pick one principle or value.

TODAY'S TL PRINCIPLE/VALUE:

PRINCIPLES

- ☐ Fear is the enemy of trust
- ☐ Really care
- ☐ People don't argue with what they help create
- ☐ There is collective wisdom in a team
- ☐ Refuse to be an adversary
- ☐ Set partnering ground rules
- ☐ To improve communica-tion, stop talking and ask good questions
- ☐ Your success is determined by how you react to the challenges you face
- ☐ There is energy in conflict
- ☐ Understand all interests

VALUES

- ☐ Trust
- ☐ Fairness
- ☐ Transparency
- ☐ Respect
- ☐ Collaboration
- ☐ Helpfuless

MY TL INTENTION TODAY:

INNER VOICE FEEDBACK:

3 **Plan for Using Your TRUSTED LEADER Intention**

I WILL INCORPORATE MY INTENTION INTO MY DAY AS FOLLOWS:

Leadership is 80% behavior and 20% know-how.
SUE DYER

4 **Observations**

WHAT ARE YOU OBSERVING AS YOU IMPLEMENT YOUR INTENTION?

-
-
-
-
-
-
-
-
-
-

5 **Evening Ritual**

WHAT DID YOU LEARN TODAY?

☐

☐

☐

☐

☐

6 **Repeat or Tweak?**

Look at your lessons learned, put an "X" next to those that did not work and a "" next to those that did work (and that you want to repeat).*

DAY25 | / /

1 Your Morning Ritual

Read/listen to your Trusted Leader Vision.

2 Your Daily TRUSTED LEADER Intention

Pick one principle or value.

TODAY'S TL PRINCIPLE/VALUE:

PRINCIPLES
- ☐ Fear is the enemy of trust
- ☐ Really care
- ☐ People don't argue with what they help create
- ☐ There is collective wisdom in a team
- ☐ Refuse to be an adversary
- ☐ Set partnering ground rules
- ☐ To improve communica-tion, stop talking and ask good questions
- ☐ Your success is determined by how you react to the challenges you face
- ☐ There is energy in conflict
- ☐ Understand all interests

VALUES
- ☐ Trust
- ☐ Fairness
- ☐ Transparency
- ☐ Respect
- ☐ Collaboration
- ☐ Helpfuless

MY TL INTENTION TODAY:

_____

_____

_____

_____

_____

_____

_____

_____

_____

INNER VOICE FEEDBACK:

_____

_____

_____

_____

_____

_____

③ Plan for Using Your TRUSTED LEADER Intention

I WILL INCORPORATE MY INTENTION INTO MY DAY AS FOLLOWS:

Leadership is 80% behavior and 20% know-how.
SUE DYER

· ·

4 Observations

WHAT ARE YOU OBSERVING AS YOU IMPLEMENT YOUR INTENTION?

-
-
-
-
-
-
-
-
-
-

5 Evening Ritual

WHAT DID YOU LEARN TODAY?

☐

☐

☐

☐

☐

6 Repeat or Tweak?

Look at your lessons learned, put an "X" next to those that did not work and a "" next to those that did work (and that you want to repeat).*

WEEKLY INSIGHTS

1 This Week's Insights

_____

_____

_____

_____

_____

_____

_____

2 This Week's Lessons Learned

_____

_____

_____

_____

_____

_____

_____

3 Things to Add to My Trusted Leader Arsenal

_____

_____

_____

_____

_____

_____

_____

Notes

DAY**26** | / /

1 Your Morning Ritual
Read/listen to your Trusted Leader Vision.

2 Your Daily **TRUSTED LEADER** Intention
Pick one principle or value.

TODAY'S TL PRINCIPLE/VALUE:

PRINCIPLES
- ☐ Fear is the enemy of trust
- ☐ Really care
- ☐ People don't argue with what they help create
- ☐ There is collective wisdom in a team
- ☐ Refuse to be an adversary
- ☐ Set partnering ground rules
- ☐ To improve communication, stop talking and ask good questions
- ☐ Your success is determined by how you react to the challenges you face
- ☐ There is energy in conflict
- ☐ Understand all interests

VALUES
- ☐ Trust
- ☐ Fairness
- ☐ Transparency
- ☐ Respect
- ☐ Collaboration
- ☐ Helpfuless

MY TL INTENTION TODAY:

INNER VOICE FEEDBACK:

3 Plan for Using Your TRUSTED LEADER Intention

I WILL INCORPORATE MY INTENTION INTO MY DAY AS FOLLOWS:

WEEK 6

The key to change ... is to let go of fear.
ROSANNE CASH

· ·

4 Observations

WHAT ARE YOU OBSERVING AS YOU IMPLEMENT YOUR INTENTION?

-
-
-
-
-
-
-
-
-
-

5 Evening Ritual

WHAT DID YOU LEARN TODAY?

☐

☐

☐

☐

☐

6 Repeat or Tweak?

Look at your lessons learned, put an "X" next to those that did not work and a "*" next to those that did work (and that you want to repeat).

DAY27 | / /

1 Your Morning Ritual
Read/listen to your Trusted Leader Vision.

2 Your Daily TRUSTED LEADER Intention
Pick one principle or value.

TODAY'S TL PRINCIPLE/VALUE:

PRINCIPLES
- ☐ Fear is the enemy of trust
- ☐ Really care
- ☐ People don't argue with what they help create
- ☐ There is collective wisdom in a team
- ☐ Refuse to be an adversary
- ☐ Set partnering ground rules
- ☐ To improve communica- tion, stop talking and ask good questions
- ☐ Your success is determined by how you react to the challenges you face
- ☐ There is energy in conflict
- ☐ Understand all interests

VALUES
- ☐ Trust
- ☐ Fairness
- ☐ Transparency
- ☐ Respect
- ☐ Collaboration
- ☐ Helpfuless

MY TL INTENTION TODAY:

_____

_____

_____

_____

_____

_____

_____

_____

INNER VOICE FEEDBACK:

_____

_____

_____

_____

_____

_____

_____

3 Plan for Using Your **TRUSTED LEADER** Intention

I WILL INCORPORATE MY INTENTION INTO MY DAY AS FOLLOWS:

WEEK 6

The key to change ... is to let go of fear.
ROSANNE CASH

4 **Observations**

WHAT ARE YOU OBSERVING AS YOU IMPLEMENT YOUR INTENTION?

-
-
-
-
-
-
-
-
-

5 Evening Ritual

WHAT DID YOU LEARN TODAY?

☐ _____

☐ _____

☐ _____

☐ _____

☐ _____

6 Repeat or Tweak?

Look at your lessons learned, put an "X" next to those that did not work and a "*" next to those that did work (and that you want to repeat).

DAY28 | / /

1 Your Morning Ritual
Read/listen to your Trusted Leader Vision.

2 Your Daily TRUSTED LEADER Intention
Pick one principle or value.

TODAY'S TL PRINCIPLE/VALUE:

PRINCIPLES
- ☐ Fear is the enemy of trust
- ☐ Really care
- ☐ People don't argue with what they help create
- ☐ There is collective wisdom in a team
- ☐ Refuse to be an adversary
- ☐ Set partnering ground rules
- ☐ To improve communication, stop talking and ask good questions
- ☐ Your success is determined by how you react to the challenges you face
- ☐ There is energy in conflict
- ☐ Understand all interests

VALUES
- ☐ Trust
- ☐ Fairness
- ☐ Transparency
- ☐ Respect
- ☐ Collaboration
- ☐ Helpfuless

MY TL INTENTION TODAY:

INNER VOICE FEEDBACK:

3 **Plan for Using Your TRUSTED LEADER Intention**

I WILL INCORPORATE MY INTENTION INTO MY DAY AS FOLLOWS:

The key to change ... is to let go of fear.
ROSANNE CASH

· ·

4 **Observations**

WHAT ARE YOU OBSERVING AS YOU IMPLEMENT YOUR INTENTION?

-
-
-
-
-
-
-
-
-
-

5 Evening Ritual

WHAT DID YOU LEARN TODAY?

☐

☐

☐

☐

☐

6 Repeat or Tweak?

Look at your lessons learned, put an "X" next to those that did not work and a "" next to those that did work (and that you want to repeat).*

DAY 29 | / /

1 Your Morning Ritual
Read/listen to your Trusted Leader Vision.

2 Your Daily TRUSTED LEADER Intention
Pick one principle or value.

TODAY'S TL PRINCIPLE/VALUE:	MY TL INTENTION TODAY:

PRINCIPLES

- ☐ Fear is the enemy of trust
- ☐ Really care
- ☐ People don't argue with what they help create
- ☐ There is collective wisdom in a team
- ☐ Refuse to be an adversary
- ☐ Set partnering ground rules
- ☐ To improve communica-tion, stop talking and ask good questions
- ☐ Your success is determined by how you react to the challenges you face
- ☐ There is energy in conflict
- ☐ Understand all interests

VALUES

- ☐ Trust
- ☐ Fairness
- ☐ Transparency
- ☐ Respect
- ☐ Collaboration
- ☐ Helpfuless

INNER VOICE FEEDBACK:

3 **Plan for Using Your TRUSTED LEADER Intention**

I WILL INCORPORATE MY INTENTION INTO MY DAY AS FOLLOWS:

The key to change ... is to let go of fear.
ROSANNE CASH

4 Observations

WHAT ARE YOU OBSERVING AS YOU IMPLEMENT YOUR INTENTION?

-
-
-
-
-
-
-
-
-
-

5 Evening Ritual

WHAT DID YOU LEARN TODAY?

☐ _____

☐ _____

☐ _____

☐ _____

☐ _____

6 Repeat or Tweak?

Look at your lessons learned, put an "X" next to those that did not work and a "*" next to those that did work (and that you want to repeat).

DAY30 | / /

1 Your Morning Ritual
Read/listen to your Trusted Leader Vision.

2 Your Daily TRUSTED LEADER Intention
Pick one principle or value.

TODAY'S TL PRINCIPLE/VALUE:

PRINCIPLES
- ☐ Fear is the enemy of trust
- ☐ Really care
- ☐ People don't argue with what they help create
- ☐ There is collective wisdom in a team
- ☐ Refuse to be an adversary
- ☐ Set partnering ground rules
- ☐ To improve communication, stop talking and ask good questions
- ☐ Your success is determined by how you react to the challenges you face
- ☐ There is energy in conflict
- ☐ Understand all interests

VALUES
- ☐ Trust
- ☐ Fairness
- ☐ Transparency
- ☐ Respect
- ☐ Collaboration
- ☐ Helpfuless

MY TL INTENTION TODAY:

INNER VOICE FEEDBACK:

3 **Plan for Using Your TRUSTED LEADER Intention**

I WILL INCORPORATE MY INTENTION INTO MY DAY AS FOLLOWS:

The key to change ... is to let go of fear.
ROSANNE CASH

· ·

4 Observations

WHAT ARE YOU OBSERVING AS YOU IMPLEMENT YOUR INTENTION?

-
-
-
-
-
-
-
-
-
-

5 Evening Ritual

WHAT DID YOU LEARN TODAY?

☐ _____

☐ _____

☐ _____

☐ _____

☐ _____

6 Repeat or Tweak?

Look at your lessons learned, put an "X" next to those that did not work and a "*" next to those that did work (and that you want to repeat).

WEEKLY INSIGHTS

1 This Week's Insights

_____

_____

_____

_____

_____

_____

_____

_____

2 This Week's Lessons Learned

_____

_____

_____

_____

_____

_____

_____

_____

3 Things to Add to My Trusted Leader Arsenal

_____

_____

_____

_____

_____

_____

Notes

DAY31 | / /

1 Your Morning Ritual
Read/listen to your Trusted Leader Vision.

2 Your Daily TRUSTED LEADER Intention
Pick one principle or value.

TODAY'S TL PRINCIPLE/VALUE:

PRINCIPLES

- ☐ Fear is the enemy of trust
- ☐ Really care
- ☐ People don't argue with what they help create
- ☐ There is collective wisdom in a team
- ☐ Refuse to be an adversary
- ☐ Set partnering ground rules
- ☐ To improve communica- tion, stop talking and ask good questions
- ☐ Your success is determined by how you react to the challenges you face
- ☐ There is energy in conflict
- ☐ Understand all interests

VALUES

- ☐ Trust
- ☐ Fairness
- ☐ Transparency
- ☐ Respect
- ☐ Collaboration
- ☐ Helpfuless

MY TL INTENTION TODAY:

INNER VOICE FEEDBACK:

3 **Plan for Using Your TRUSTED LEADER Intention**

I WILL INCORPORATE MY INTENTION INTO MY DAY AS FOLLOWS:

The quality of your practice determines the caliber of your performance.
ROBIN SHARMA

④ Observations

WHAT ARE YOU OBSERVING AS YOU IMPLEMENT YOUR INTENTION?

-

-

-

-

-

-

-

-

-

-

5 Evening Ritual

WHAT DID YOU LEARN TODAY?

☐

☐

☐

☐

☐

6 Repeat or Tweak?

Look at your lessons learned, put an "X" next to those that did not work and a "*" next to those that did work (and that you want to repeat).

DAY32 | / /

① Your Morning Ritual

Read/listen to your Trusted Leader Vision.

② Your Daily TRUSTED LEADER Intention

Pick one principle or value.

TODAY'S TL PRINCIPLE/VALUE:

PRINCIPLES

- ☐ Fear is the enemy of trust
- ☐ Really care
- ☐ People don't argue with what they help create
- ☐ There is collective wisdom in a team
- ☐ Refuse to be an adversary
- ☐ Set partnering ground rules
- ☐ To improve communication, stop talking and ask good questions
- ☐ Your success is determined by how you react to the challenges you face
- ☐ There is energy in conflict
- ☐ Understand all interests

VALUES

- ☐ Trust
- ☐ Fairness
- ☐ Transparency
- ☐ Respect
- ☐ Collaboration
- ☐ Helpfuless

MY TL INTENTION TODAY:

_____

_____

_____

_____

_____

_____

_____

_____

INNER VOICE FEEDBACK:

_____

_____

_____

_____

_____

_____

_____

3 Plan for Using Your TRUSTED LEADER Intention

I WILL INCORPORATE MY INTENTION INTO MY DAY AS FOLLOWS:

The quality of your practice determines the caliber of your performance.
ROBIN SHARMA

4 Observations

WHAT ARE YOU OBSERVING AS YOU IMPLEMENT YOUR INTENTION?

-
-
-
-
-
-
-
-
-
-

5 **Evening Ritual**

WHAT DID YOU LEARN TODAY?

☐

☐

☐

☐

☐

6 **Repeat or Tweak?**

Look at your lessons learned, put an "X" next to those that did not work and a "*" next to those that did work (and that you want to repeat).

DAY33 | / /

1 Your Morning Ritual
Read/listen to your Trusted Leader Vision.

2 Your Daily TRUSTED LEADER Intention
Pick one principle or value.

TODAY'S TL PRINCIPLE/VALUE:

PRINCIPLES
- ☐ Fear is the enemy of trust
- ☐ Really care
- ☐ People don't argue with what they help create
- ☐ There is collective wisdom in a team
- ☐ Refuse to be an adversary
- ☐ Set partnering ground rules
- ☐ To improve communica- tion, stop talking and ask good questions
- ☐ Your success is determined by how you react to the challenges you face
- ☐ There is energy in conflict
- ☐ Understand all interests

VALUES
- ☐ Trust
- ☐ Fairness
- ☐ Transparency
- ☐ Respect
- ☐ Collaboration
- ☐ Helpfuless

MY TL INTENTION TODAY:

INNER VOICE FEEDBACK:

3 Plan for Using Your **TRUSTED LEADER** Intention

I WILL INCORPORATE MY INTENTION INTO MY DAY AS FOLLOWS:

The quality of your practice determines the caliber of your performance.
ROBIN SHARMA

4 **Observations**

WHAT ARE YOU OBSERVING AS YOU IMPLEMENT YOUR INTENTION?

-
-
-
-
-
-
-
-
-
-

5 **Evening Ritual**

WHAT DID YOU LEARN TODAY?

☐

☐

☐

☐

☐

6 **Repeat or Tweak?**

Look at your lessons learned, put an "X" next to those that did not work and a "*" next to those that did work (and that you want to repeat).

DAY34 | / /

1 Your Morning Ritual
Read/listen to your Trusted Leader Vision.

2 Your Daily TRUSTED LEADER Intention
Pick one principle or value.

TODAY'S TL PRINCIPLE/VALUE:

PRINCIPLES
- ☐ Fear is the enemy of trust
- ☐ Really care
- ☐ People don't argue with what they help create
- ☐ There is collective wisdom in a team
- ☐ Refuse to be an adversary
- ☐ Set partnering ground rules
- ☐ To improve communication, stop talking and ask good questions
- ☐ Your success is determined by how you react to the challenges you face
- ☐ There is energy in conflict
- ☐ Understand all interests

VALUES
- ☐ Trust
- ☐ Fairness
- ☐ Transparency
- ☐ Respect
- ☐ Collaboration
- ☐ Helpfuless

MY TL INTENTION TODAY:

INNER VOICE FEEDBACK:

3 **Plan for Using Your TRUSTED LEADER Intention**

I WILL INCORPORATE MY INTENTION INTO MY DAY AS FOLLOWS:

The quality of your practice determines the caliber of your performance.
ROBIN SHARMA

4 Observations

WHAT ARE YOU OBSERVING AS YOU IMPLEMENT YOUR INTENTION?

-
-
-
-
-
-
-
-
-
-

5 Evening Ritual

WHAT DID YOU LEARN TODAY?

☐

☐

☐

☐

☐

6 Repeat or Tweak?

Look at your lessons learned, put an "X" next to those that did not work and a "" next to those that did work (and that you want to repeat).*

DAY35 | / /

1 Your Morning Ritual
Read/listen to your Trusted Leader Vision.

2 Your Daily TRUSTED LEADER Intention
Pick one principle or value.

TODAY'S TL PRINCIPLE/VALUE:

PRINCIPLES
- [ ] Fear is the enemy of trust
- [ ] Really care
- [ ] People don't argue with what they help create
- [ ] There is collective wisdom in a team
- [ ] Refuse to be an adversary
- [ ] Set partnering ground rules
- [ ] To improve communication, stop talking and ask good questions
- [ ] Your success is determined by how you react to the challenges you face
- [ ] There is energy in conflict
- [ ] Understand all interests

VALUES
- [ ] Trust
- [ ] Fairness
- [ ] Transparency
- [ ] Respect
- [ ] Collaboration
- [ ] Helpfuless

MY TL INTENTION TODAY:

_____

_____

_____

_____

_____

_____

_____

_____

INNER VOICE FEEDBACK:

_____

3 **Plan for Using Your TRUSTED LEADER Intention**

I WILL INCORPORATE MY INTENTION INTO MY DAY AS FOLLOWS:

The quality of your practice determines the caliber of your performance.
ROBIN SHARMA

4 Observations

WHAT ARE YOU OBSERVING AS YOU IMPLEMENT YOUR INTENTION?

-

-

-

-

-

-

-

-

-

-

5 Evening Ritual

WHAT DID YOU LEARN TODAY?

☐ _____

☐ _____

☐ _____

☐ _____

☐ _____

6 Repeat or Tweak?

Look at your lessons learned, put an "X" next to those that did not work and a "" next to those that did work (and that you want to repeat).*

WEEK 7

WEEKLY INSIGHTS

1 This Week's Insights

_____
_____
_____
_____
_____
_____
_____
_____

2 This Week's Lessons Learned

_____
_____
_____
_____
_____
_____
_____

3 Things to Add to My Trusted Leader Arsenal

_____
_____
_____
_____
_____
_____

Notes

DAY36 | / /

① Your Morning Ritual
Read/listen to your Trusted Leader Vision.

② Your Daily TRUSTED LEADER Intention
Pick one principle or value.

TODAY'S TL PRINCIPLE/VALUE: MY TL INTENTION TODAY:

PRINCIPLES

- ☐ Fear is the enemy of trust
- ☐ Really care
- ☐ People don't argue with what they help create
- ☐ There is collective wisdom in a team
- ☐ Refuse to be an adversary
- ☐ Set partnering ground rules
- ☐ To improve communication, stop talking and ask good questions
- ☐ Your success is determined by how you react to the challenges you face
- ☐ There is energy in conflict
- ☐ Understand all interests

VALUES

- ☐ Trust
- ☐ Fairness
- ☐ Transparency
- ☐ Respect
- ☐ Collaboration
- ☐ Helpfuless

INNER VOICE FEEDBACK:

3 Plan for Using Your **TRUSTED LEADER** Intention

I WILL INCORPORATE MY INTENTION INTO MY DAY AS FOLLOWS:

WEEK 8

Transformation isn't a future event, but a present day activity.
JILLIAN MICHAELS

4 Observations

WHAT ARE YOU OBSERVING AS YOU IMPLEMENT YOUR INTENTION?

-
-
-
-
-
-
-
-
-
-

5 Evening Ritual

WHAT DID YOU LEARN TODAY?

☐

☐

☐

☐

☐

6 Repeat or Tweak?
Look at your lessons learned, put an "X" next to those that did not work and a "*" next to those that did work (and that you want to repeat).

DAY37 | / /

① Your Morning Ritual
Read/listen to your Trusted Leader Vision.

② Your Daily TRUSTED LEADER Intention
Pick one principle or value.

TODAY'S TL PRINCIPLE/VALUE:

PRINCIPLES	VALUES
☐ Fear is the enemy of trust	☐ Trust
☐ Really care	☐ Fairness
☐ People don't argue with what they help create	☐ Transparency
	☐ Respect
☐ There is collective wisdom in a team	☐ Collaboration
☐ Refuse to be an adversary	☐ Helpfuless
☐ Set partnering ground rules	
☐ To improve communication, stop talking and ask good questions	
☐ Your success is determined by how you react to the challenges you face	
☐ There is energy in conflict	
☐ Understand all interests	

MY TL INTENTION TODAY:

INNER VOICE FEEDBACK:

3 **Plan for Using Your TRUSTED LEADER Intention**

I WILL INCORPORATE MY INTENTION INTO MY DAY AS FOLLOWS:

Transformation isn't a future event, but a present day activity.
JILLIAN MICHAELS

4 Observations

WHAT ARE YOU OBSERVING AS YOU IMPLEMENT YOUR INTENTION?

-
-
-
-
-
-
-
-
-
-

⑤ Evening Ritual

WHAT DID YOU LEARN TODAY?

☐ _____

☐ _____

☐ _____

☐ _____

☐ _____

⑥ Repeat or Tweak?

Look at your lessons learned, put an "X" next to those that did not work and a "" next to those that did work (and that you want to repeat).*

DAY38 | / /

1 Your Morning Ritual

Read/listen to your Trusted Leader Vision.

2 Your Daily **TRUSTED LEADER** Intention

Pick one principle or value.

TODAY'S TL PRINCIPLE/VALUE:

MY TL INTENTION TODAY:

PRINCIPLES

- ☐ Fear is the enemy of trust
- ☐ Really care
- ☐ People don't argue with what they help create
- ☐ There is collective wisdom in a team
- ☐ Refuse to be an adversary
- ☐ Set partnering ground rules
- ☐ To improve communica-tion, stop talking and ask good questions
- ☐ Your success is determined by how you react to the challenges you face
- ☐ There is energy in conflict
- ☐ Understand all interests

VALUES

- ☐ Trust
- ☐ Fairness
- ☐ Transparency
- ☐ Respect
- ☐ Collaboration
- ☐ Helpfuless

INNER VOICE FEEDBACK:

3 **Plan for Using Your TRUSTED LEADER Intention**

I WILL INCORPORATE MY INTENTION INTO MY DAY AS FOLLOWS:

Transformation isn't a future event, but a present day activity.
JILLIAN MICHAELS

4 Observations

WHAT ARE YOU OBSERVING AS YOU IMPLEMENT YOUR INTENTION?

-
-
-
-
-
-
-
-
-

5 **Evening Ritual**

WHAT DID YOU LEARN TODAY?

☐

☐

☐

☐

☐

6 **Repeat or Tweak?**
Look at your lessons learned, put an "X" next to those that did not work and a "*" next to those that did work (and that you want to repeat).

DAY39 | / /

1 Your Morning Ritual
Read/listen to your Trusted Leader Vision.

2 Your Daily TRUSTED LEADER Intention
Pick one principle or value.

TODAY'S TL PRINCIPLE/VALUE:

PRINCIPLES
- ☐ Fear is the enemy of trust
- ☐ Really care
- ☐ People don't argue with what they help create
- ☐ There is collective wisdom in a team
- ☐ Refuse to be an adversary
- ☐ Set partnering ground rules
- ☐ To improve communication, stop talking and ask good questions
- ☐ Your success is determined by how you react to the challenges you face
- ☐ There is energy in conflict
- ☐ Understand all interests

VALUES
- ☐ Trust
- ☐ Fairness
- ☐ Transparency
- ☐ Respect
- ☐ Collaboration
- ☐ Helpfuless

MY TL INTENTION TODAY:

INNER VOICE FEEDBACK:

3 Plan for Using Your TRUSTED LEADER Intention

I WILL INCORPORATE MY INTENTION INTO MY DAY AS FOLLOWS:

WEEK 8

4 **Observations**

WHAT ARE YOU OBSERVING AS YOU IMPLEMENT YOUR INTENTION?

-
-
-
-
-
-
-
-
-

5 **Evening Ritual**

WHAT DID YOU LEARN TODAY?

☐ _____

☐ _____

☐ _____

☐ _____

☐ _____

6 **Repeat or Tweak?**

Look at your lessons learned, put an "X" next to those that did not work and a "" next to those that did work (and that you want to repeat).*

DAY40 | / /

1 Your Morning Ritual
Read/listen to your Trusted Leader Vision.

2 Your Daily TRUSTED LEADER Intention
Pick one principle or value.

TODAY'S TL PRINCIPLE/VALUE:

PRINCIPLES
- ☐ Fear is the enemy of trust
- ☐ Really care
- ☐ People don't argue with what they help create
- ☐ There is collective wisdom in a team
- ☐ Refuse to be an adversary
- ☐ Set partnering ground rules
- ☐ To improve communication, stop talking and ask good questions
- ☐ Your success is determined by how you react to the challenges you face
- ☐ There is energy in conflict
- ☐ Understand all interests

VALUES
- ☐ Trust
- ☐ Fairness
- ☐ Transparency
- ☐ Respect
- ☐ Collaboration
- ☐ Helpfuless

MY TL INTENTION TODAY:

INNER VOICE FEEDBACK:

3 **Plan for Using Your TRUSTED LEADER Intention**

I WILL INCORPORATE MY INTENTION INTO MY DAY AS FOLLOWS:

Transformation isn't a future event, but a present day activity.
JILLIAN MICHAELS

4 **Observations**

WHAT ARE YOU OBSERVING AS YOU IMPLEMENT YOUR INTENTION?

-
-
-
-
-
-
-
-
-

5 Evening Ritual

WHAT DID YOU LEARN TODAY?

☐

☐

☐

☐

☐

6 Repeat or Tweak?

Look at your lessons learned, put an "X" next to those that did not work and a "" next to those that did work (and that you want to repeat).*

WEEKLY INSIGHTS

1 **This Week's Insights**

_____

_____

_____

_____

_____

_____

_____

2 **This Week's Lessons Learned**

_____

_____

_____

_____

_____

_____

_____

3 **Things to Add to My Trusted Leader Arsenal**

_____

_____

_____

_____

_____

_____

Notes

DAY41 | / /

1 Your Morning Ritual
Read/listen to your Trusted Leader Vision.

2 Your Daily TRUSTED LEADER Intention
Pick one principle or value.

TODAY'S TL PRINCIPLE/VALUE:

PRINCIPLES
- ☐ Fear is the enemy of trust
- ☐ Really care
- ☐ People don't argue with what they help create
- ☐ There is collective wisdom in a team
- ☐ Refuse to be an adversary
- ☐ Set partnering ground rules
- ☐ To improve communication, stop talking and ask good questions
- ☐ Your success is determined by how you react to the challenges you face
- ☐ There is energy in conflict
- ☐ Understand all interests

VALUES
- ☐ Trust
- ☐ Fairness
- ☐ Transparency
- ☐ Respect
- ☐ Collaboration
- ☐ Helpfuless

MY TL INTENTION TODAY:

INNER VOICE FEEDBACK:

3 Plan for Using Your **TRUSTED LEADER** Intention

I WILL INCORPORATE MY INTENTION INTO MY DAY AS FOLLOWS:

_____

_____

_____

_____

_____

_____

_____

_____

_____

_____

_____

_____

_____

_____

_____

_____

_____

_____

_____

_____

71% of companies say their leaders are not ready to lead their organizations into the future.
BRANDON HALL GROUP

4 **Observations**

WHAT ARE YOU OBSERVING AS YOU IMPLEMENT YOUR INTENTION?

-
-
-
-
-
-
-
-
-
-

5 Evening Ritual

WHAT DID YOU LEARN TODAY?

☐ _____

☐ _____

☐ _____

☐ _____

☐ _____

6 Repeat or Tweak?

Look at your lessons learned, put an "X" next to those that did not work and a "" next to those that did work (and that you want to repeat).*

DAY42 | / /

1 Your Morning Ritual
Read/listen to your Trusted Leader Vision.

2 Your Daily TRUSTED LEADER Intention
Pick one principle or value.

TODAY'S TL PRINCIPLE/VALUE:

PRINCIPLES
- ☐ Fear is the enemy of trust
- ☐ Really care
- ☐ People don't argue with what they help create
- ☐ There is collective wisdom in a team
- ☐ Refuse to be an adversary
- ☐ Set partnering ground rules
- ☐ To improve communica-tion, stop talking and ask good questions
- ☐ Your success is determined by how you react to the challenges you face
- ☐ There is energy in conflict
- ☐ Understand all interests

VALUES
- ☐ Trust
- ☐ Fairness
- ☐ Transparency
- ☐ Respect
- ☐ Collaboration
- ☐ Helpfuless

MY TL INTENTION TODAY:

INNER VOICE FEEDBACK:

3 **Plan for Using Your TRUSTED LEADER Intention**

I WILL INCORPORATE MY INTENTION INTO MY DAY AS FOLLOWS:

71% of companies say their leaders are not ready to lead their organizations into the future.
BRANDON HALL GROUP

··

4 **Observations**

WHAT ARE YOU OBSERVING AS YOU IMPLEMENT YOUR INTENTION?

-
-
-
-
-
-
-
-
-
-

5 Evening Ritual

WHAT DID YOU LEARN TODAY?

☐

☐

☐

☐

☐

6 Repeat or Tweak?

Look at your lessons learned, put an "X" next to those that did not work and a "" next to those that did work (and that you want to repeat).*

DAY43 | / /

1 Your Morning Ritual
Read/listen to your Trusted Leader Vision.

2 Your Daily TRUSTED LEADER Intention
Pick one principle or value.

TODAY'S TL PRINCIPLE/VALUE:

PRINCIPLES
- ☐ Fear is the enemy of trust
- ☐ Really care
- ☐ People don't argue with what they help create
- ☐ There is collective wisdom in a team
- ☐ Refuse to be an adversary
- ☐ Set partnering ground rules
- ☐ To improve communication, stop talking and ask good questions
- ☐ Your success is determined by how you react to the challenges you face
- ☐ There is energy in conflict
- ☐ Understand all interests

VALUES
- ☐ Trust
- ☐ Fairness
- ☐ Transparency
- ☐ Respect
- ☐ Collaboration
- ☐ Helpfuless

MY TL INTENTION TODAY:

INNER VOICE FEEDBACK:

3 **Plan for Using Your TRUSTED LEADER Intention**

I WILL INCORPORATE MY INTENTION INTO MY DAY AS FOLLOWS:

71% of companies say their leaders are not ready to lead their organizations into the future.
BRANDON HALL GROUP

④ Observations

WHAT ARE YOU OBSERVING AS YOU IMPLEMENT YOUR INTENTION?

-
-
-
-
-
-
-
-
-
-

5 **Evening Ritual**

WHAT DID YOU LEARN TODAY?

☐

☐

☐

☐

☐

6 **Repeat or Tweak?**

Look at your lessons learned, put an "X" next to those that did not work and a "" next to those that did work (and that you want to repeat).*

DAY44 | / /

1 Your Morning Ritual
Read/listen to your Trusted Leader Vision.

2 Your Daily TRUSTED LEADER Intention
Pick one principle or value.

TODAY'S TL PRINCIPLE/VALUE:

PRINCIPLES
- [ ] Fear is the enemy of trust
- [ ] Really care
- [ ] People don't argue with what they help create
- [ ] There is collective wisdom in a team
- [ ] Refuse to be an adversary
- [ ] Set partnering ground rules
- [ ] To improve communication, stop talking and ask good questions
- [ ] Your success is determined by how you react to the challenges you face
- [ ] There is energy in conflict
- [ ] Understand all interests

VALUES
- [ ] Trust
- [ ] Fairness
- [ ] Transparency
- [ ] Respect
- [ ] Collaboration
- [ ] Helpfuless

MY TL INTENTION TODAY:

_____

_____

_____

_____

_____

_____

_____

_____

INNER VOICE FEEDBACK:

_____

_____

_____

_____

_____

_____

_____

3 **Plan for Using Your TRUSTED LEADER Intention**

I WILL INCORPORATE MY INTENTION INTO MY DAY AS FOLLOWS:

71% of companies say their leaders are not ready to lead their organizations into the future.
BRANDON HALL GROUP

4 Observations

WHAT ARE YOU OBSERVING AS YOU IMPLEMENT YOUR INTENTION?

-
-
-
-
-
-
-
-
-
-

5 **Evening Ritual**

WHAT DID YOU LEARN TODAY?

☐

☐

☐

☐

☐

6 **Repeat or Tweak?**

Look at your lessons learned, put an "X" next to those that did not work and a "" next to those that did work (and that you want to repeat).*

DAY45 | / /

1 Your Morning Ritual
Read/listen to your Trusted Leader Vision.

2 Your Daily TRUSTED LEADER Intention
Pick one principle or value.

TODAY'S TL PRINCIPLE/VALUE:

PRINCIPLES

- ☐ Fear is the enemy of trust
- ☐ Really care
- ☐ People don't argue with what they help create
- ☐ There is collective wisdom in a team
- ☐ Refuse to be an adversary
- ☐ Set partnering ground rules
- ☐ To improve communication, stop talking and ask good questions
- ☐ Your success is determined by how you react to the challenges you face
- ☐ There is energy in conflict
- ☐ Understand all interests

VALUES

- ☐ Trust
- ☐ Fairness
- ☐ Transparency
- ☐ Respect
- ☐ Collaboration
- ☐ Helpfuless

MY TL INTENTION TODAY:

INNER VOICE FEEDBACK:

3 Plan for Using Your TRUSTED LEADER Intention

I WILL INCORPORATE MY INTENTION INTO MY DAY AS FOLLOWS:

71% of companies say their leaders are not ready to lead their organizations into the future.
BRANDON HALL GROUP

④ Observations

WHAT ARE YOU OBSERVING AS YOU IMPLEMENT YOUR INTENTION?

-
-
-
-
-
-
-
-
-
-

5 Evening Ritual

WHAT DID YOU LEARN TODAY?

☐

☐

☐

☐

☐

6 Repeat or Tweak?

Look at your lessons learned, put an "X" next to those that did not work and a "" next to those that did work (and that you want to repeat).*

WEEKLY INSIGHTS

1 This Week's Insights

_____
_____
_____
_____
_____
_____
_____
_____

2 This Week's Lessons Learned

_____
_____
_____
_____
_____
_____
_____
_____

3 Things to Add to My Trusted Leader Arsenal

_____
_____
_____
_____
_____
_____

Notes

DAY46 | / /

1 Your Morning Ritual
Read/listen to your Trusted Leader Vision.

2 Your Daily TRUSTED LEADER Intention
Pick one principle or value.

TODAY'S TL PRINCIPLE/VALUE:

PRINCIPLES
- ☐ Fear is the enemy of trust
- ☐ Really care
- ☐ People don't argue with what they help create
- ☐ There is collective wisdom in a team
- ☐ Refuse to be an adversary
- ☐ Set partnering ground rules
- ☐ To improve communica-tion, stop talking and ask good questions
- ☐ Your success is determined by how you react to the challenges you face
- ☐ There is energy in conflict
- ☐ Understand all interests

VALUES
- ☐ Trust
- ☐ Fairness
- ☐ Transparency
- ☐ Respect
- ☐ Collaboration
- ☐ Helpfuless

MY TL INTENTION TODAY:

INNER VOICE FEEDBACK:

3 **Plan for Using Your TRUSTED LEADER Intention**

I WILL INCORPORATE MY INTENTION INTO MY DAY AS FOLLOWS:

The culture of a company is the sum of the behaviors of all its people.
MICHAEL KOULY

4 Observations

WHAT ARE YOU OBSERVING AS YOU IMPLEMENT YOUR INTENTION?

-
-
-
-
-
-
-
-
-
-

5 Evening Ritual

WHAT DID YOU LEARN TODAY?

☐ _____

☐ _____

☐ _____

☐ _____

☐ _____

6 Repeat or Tweak?

Look at your lessons learned, put an "X" next to those that did not work and a "" next to those that did work (and that you want to repeat).*

DAY47 | / /

1 Your Morning Ritual
Read/listen to your Trusted Leader Vision.

2 Your Daily TRUSTED LEADER Intention
Pick one principle or value.

TODAY'S TL PRINCIPLE/VALUE:

PRINCIPLES
- ☐ Fear is the enemy of trust
- ☐ Really care
- ☐ People don't argue with what they help create
- ☐ There is collective wisdom in a team
- ☐ Refuse to be an adversary
- ☐ Set partnering ground rules
- ☐ To improve communica- tion, stop talking and ask good questions
- ☐ Your success is determined by how you react to the challenges you face
- ☐ There is energy in conflict
- ☐ Understand all interests

VALUES
- ☐ Trust
- ☐ Fairness
- ☐ Transparency
- ☐ Respect
- ☐ Collaboration
- ☐ Helpfuless

MY TL INTENTION TODAY:

INNER VOICE FEEDBACK:

3 **Plan for Using Your TRUSTED LEADER Intention**

I WILL INCORPORATE MY INTENTION INTO MY DAY AS FOLLOWS:

The culture of a company is the sum of the behaviors of all its people.
MICHAEL KOULY

. . . .

4 Observations

WHAT ARE YOU OBSERVING AS YOU IMPLEMENT YOUR INTENTION?

-
-
-
-
-
-
-
-
-
-

5 **Evening Ritual**

WHAT DID YOU LEARN TODAY?

- ☐

- ☐

- ☐

- ☐

- ☐

6 **Repeat or Tweak?**

Look at your lessons learned, put an "X" next to those that did not work and a "" next to those that did work (and that you want to repeat).*

DAY48 | / /

1 Your Morning Ritual
Read/listen to your Trusted Leader Vision.

2 Your Daily TRUSTED LEADER Intention
Pick one principle or value.

TODAY'S TL PRINCIPLE/VALUE:

PRINCIPLES
- ☐ Fear is the enemy of trust
- ☐ Really care
- ☐ People don't argue with what they help create
- ☐ There is collective wisdom in a team
- ☐ Refuse to be an adversary
- ☐ Set partnering ground rules
- ☐ To improve communication, stop talking and ask good questions
- ☐ Your success is determined by how you react to the challenges you face
- ☐ There is energy in conflict
- ☐ Understand all interests

VALUES
- ☐ Trust
- ☐ Fairness
- ☐ Transparency
- ☐ Respect
- ☐ Collaboration
- ☐ Helpfuless

MY TL INTENTION TODAY:

INNER VOICE FEEDBACK:

(3) Plan for Using Your TRUSTED LEADER Intention

I WILL INCORPORATE MY INTENTION INTO MY DAY AS FOLLOWS:

The culture of a company is the sum of the behaviors of all its people.
MICHAEL KOULY

4 Observations

WHAT ARE YOU OBSERVING AS YOU IMPLEMENT YOUR INTENTION?

-
-
-
-
-
-
-
-
-
-

5 **Evening Ritual**

WHAT DID YOU LEARN TODAY?

☐

☐

☐

☐

☐

6 **Repeat or Tweak?**

Look at your lessons learned, put an "X" next to those that did not work and a "" next to those that did work (and that you want to repeat).*

DAY49 | / /
···

1 **Your Morning Ritual**

Read/listen to your Trusted Leader Vision.

2 **Your Daily TRUSTED LEADER Intention**

Pick one principle or value.

TODAY'S TL PRINCIPLE/VALUE:

PRINCIPLES

- ☐ Fear is the enemy of trust
- ☐ Really care
- ☐ People don't argue with what they help create
- ☐ There is collective wisdom in a team
- ☐ Refuse to be an adversary
- ☐ Set partnering ground rules
- ☐ To improve communication, stop talking and ask good questions
- ☐ Your success is determined by how you react to the challenges you face
- ☐ There is energy in conflict
- ☐ Understand all interests

VALUES

- ☐ Trust
- ☐ Fairness
- ☐ Transparency
- ☐ Respect
- ☐ Collaboration
- ☐ Helpfuless

MY TL INTENTION TODAY:

INNER VOICE FEEDBACK:

3 Plan for Using Your **TRUSTED LEADER** Intention

I WILL INCORPORATE MY INTENTION INTO MY DAY AS FOLLOWS:

The culture of a company is the sum of the behaviors of all its people.
MICHAEL KOULY

4 Observations

WHAT ARE YOU OBSERVING AS YOU IMPLEMENT YOUR INTENTION?

-
-
-
-
-
-
-
-
-
-

5 **Evening Ritual**

WHAT DID YOU LEARN TODAY?

☐ _____

☐ _____

☐ _____

☐ _____

☐ _____

6 **Repeat or Tweak?**

Look at your lessons learned, put an "X" next to those that did not work and a "*" next to those that did work (and that you want to repeat).

DAY50 | / /

1 Your Morning Ritual
Read/listen to your Trusted Leader Vision.

2 Your Daily TRUSTED LEADER Intention
Pick one principle or value.

TODAY'S TL PRINCIPLE/VALUE:

PRINCIPLES
- ☐ Fear is the enemy of trust
- ☐ Really care
- ☐ People don't argue with what they help create
- ☐ There is collective wisdom in a team
- ☐ Refuse to be an adversary
- ☐ Set partnering ground rules
- ☐ To improve communication, stop talking and ask good questions
- ☐ Your success is determined by how you react to the challenges you face
- ☐ There is energy in conflict
- ☐ Understand all interests

VALUES
- ☐ Trust
- ☐ Fairness
- ☐ Transparency
- ☐ Respect
- ☐ Collaboration
- ☐ Helpfuless

MY TL INTENTION TODAY:

INNER VOICE FEEDBACK:

3 **Plan for Using Your TRUSTED LEADER Intention**

I WILL INCORPORATE MY INTENTION INTO MY DAY AS FOLLOWS:

The culture of a company is the sum of the behaviors of all its people.
MICHAEL KOULY

· ·

4 **Observations**

WHAT ARE YOU OBSERVING AS YOU IMPLEMENT YOUR INTENTION?

-
-
-
-
-
-
-
-
-
-

5 **Evening Ritual**

WHAT DID YOU LEARN TODAY?

☐

☐

☐

☐

☐

6 **Repeat or Tweak?**

Look at your lessons learned, put an "X" next to those that did not work and a "" next to those that did work (and that you want to repeat).*

WEEKLY INSIGHTS

1 **This Week's Insights**

_____
_____
_____
_____
_____
_____
_____
_____

2 **This Week's Lessons Learned**

_____
_____
_____
_____
_____
_____
_____
_____

3 **Things to Add to My Trusted Leader Arsenal**

_____
_____
_____
_____
_____
_____
_____

Notes

DAY51 | / /

1 Your Morning Ritual
Read/listen to your Trusted Leader Vision.

2 Your Daily TRUSTED LEADER Intention
Pick one principle or value.

TODAY'S TL PRINCIPLE/VALUE:

PRINCIPLES
- ☐ Fear is the enemy of trust
- ☐ Really care
- ☐ People don't argue with what they help create
- ☐ There is collective wisdom in a team
- ☐ Refuse to be an adversary
- ☐ Set partnering ground rules
- ☐ To improve communication, stop talking and ask good questions
- ☐ Your success is determined by how you react to the challenges you face
- ☐ There is energy in conflict
- ☐ Understand all interests

VALUES
- ☐ Trust
- ☐ Fairness
- ☐ Transparency
- ☐ Respect
- ☐ Collaboration
- ☐ Helpfuless

MY TL INTENTION TODAY:

_____

_____

_____

_____

_____

_____

_____

_____

_____

INNER VOICE FEEDBACK:

_____

_____

_____

_____

_____

_____

_____

3 Plan for Using Your **TRUSTED LEADER** Intention

I WILL INCORPORATE MY INTENTION INTO MY DAY AS FOLLOWS:

Everything can be taken from a man but one thing: to choose one's attitude in any given circumstance.
VIKTOR E. FRANKL

4 Observations

WHAT ARE YOU OBSERVING AS YOU IMPLEMENT YOUR INTENTION?

-
-
-
-
-
-
-
-
-
-

5 **Evening Ritual**

WHAT DID YOU LEARN TODAY?

☐

☐

☐

☐

☐

6 **Repeat or Tweak?**

Look at your lessons learned, put an "X" next to those that did not work and a "*" next to those that did work (and that you want to repeat).

DAY52 | / /

1 Your Morning Ritual
Read/listen to your Trusted Leader Vision.

2 Your Daily TRUSTED LEADER Intention
Pick one principle or value.

TODAY'S TL PRINCIPLE/VALUE:

PRINCIPLES
- ☐ Fear is the enemy of trust
- ☐ Really care
- ☐ People don't argue with what they help create
- ☐ There is collective wisdom in a team
- ☐ Refuse to be an adversary
- ☐ Set partnering ground rules
- ☐ To improve communication, stop talking and ask good questions
- ☐ Your success is determined by how you react to the challenges you face
- ☐ There is energy in conflict
- ☐ Understand all interests

VALUES
- ☐ Trust
- ☐ Fairness
- ☐ Transparency
- ☐ Respect
- ☐ Collaboration
- ☐ Helpfuless

MY TL INTENTION TODAY:

_____

_____

_____

_____

_____

_____

_____

_____

INNER VOICE FEEDBACK:

_____

_____

_____

_____

_____

_____

_____

3 Plan for Using Your **TRUSTED LEADER** Intention

I WILL INCORPORATE MY INTENTION INTO MY DAY AS FOLLOWS:

Everything can be taken from a man but one thing: to choose one's attitude in any given circumstance.
VIKTOR E. FRANKL

4 Observations

WHAT ARE YOU OBSERVING AS YOU IMPLEMENT YOUR INTENTION?

-
-
-
-
-
-
-
-
-
-

5 Evening Ritual

WHAT DID YOU LEARN TODAY?

☐

☐

☐

☐

☐

6 Repeat or Tweak?

Look at your lessons learned, put an "X" next to those that did not work and a "*" next to those that did work (and that you want to repeat).

DAY53 | / /

1 Your Morning Ritual
Read/listen to your Trusted Leader Vision.

2 Your Daily TRUSTED LEADER Intention
Pick one principle or value.

TODAY'S TL PRINCIPLE/VALUE:

PRINCIPLES
- ☐ Fear is the enemy of trust
- ☐ Really care
- ☐ People don't argue with what they help create
- ☐ There is collective wisdom in a team
- ☐ Refuse to be an adversary
- ☐ Set partnering ground rules
- ☐ To improve communica-tion, stop talking and ask good questions
- ☐ Your success is determined by how you react to the challenges you face
- ☐ There is energy in conflict
- ☐ Understand all interests

VALUES
- ☐ Trust
- ☐ Fairness
- ☐ Transparency
- ☐ Respect
- ☐ Collaboration
- ☐ Helpfuless

MY TL INTENTION TODAY:

_____

_____

_____

_____

_____

_____

_____

_____

INNER VOICE FEEDBACK:

_____

_____

_____

_____

_____

_____

· ·

3 **Plan for Using Your TRUSTED LEADER Intention**

I WILL INCORPORATE MY INTENTION INTO MY DAY AS FOLLOWS:

Everything can be taken from a man but one thing: to choose one's attitude in any given circumstance.
VIKTOR E. FRANKL

4 Observations

WHAT ARE YOU OBSERVING AS YOU IMPLEMENT YOUR INTENTION?

-
-
-
-
-
-
-
-
-
-

5 Evening Ritual

WHAT DID YOU LEARN TODAY?

☐ _____

☐ _____

☐ _____

☐ _____

☐ _____

6 Repeat or Tweak?

Look at your lessons learned, put an "X" next to those that did not work and a "*" next to those that did work (and that you want to repeat).

DAY54 | / /

1 Your Morning Ritual
Read/listen to your Trusted Leader Vision.

2 Your Daily TRUSTED LEADER Intention
Pick one principle or value.

TODAY'S TL PRINCIPLE/VALUE:

PRINCIPLES
- ☐ Fear is the enemy of trust
- ☐ Really care
- ☐ People don't argue with what they help create
- ☐ There is collective wisdom in a team
- ☐ Refuse to be an adversary
- ☐ Set partnering ground rules
- ☐ To improve communica-tion, stop talking and ask good questions
- ☐ Your success is determined by how you react to the challenges you face
- ☐ There is energy in conflict
- ☐ Understand all interests

VALUES
- ☐ Trust
- ☐ Fairness
- ☐ Transparency
- ☐ Respect
- ☐ Collaboration
- ☐ Helpfuless

MY TL INTENTION TODAY:

_____

_____

_____

_____

_____

_____

_____

_____

INNER VOICE FEEDBACK:

_____

_____

_____

_____

_____

_____

_____

3 Plan for Using Your **TRUSTED LEADER** Intention

I WILL INCORPORATE MY INTENTION INTO MY DAY AS FOLLOWS:

Everything can be taken from a man but one thing: to choose one's attitude in any given circumstance.
VIKTOR E. FRANKL

4 Observations

WHAT ARE YOU OBSERVING AS YOU IMPLEMENT YOUR INTENTION?

-
-
-
-
-
-
-
-
-
-

5 **Evening Ritual**

WHAT DID YOU LEARN TODAY?

☐

☐

☐

☐

☐

6 **Repeat or Tweak?**
Look at your lessons learned, put an "X" next to those that did not work and a "" next to those that did work (and that you want to repeat).*

DAY55 | / /

1 Your Morning Ritual
Read/listen to your Trusted Leader Vision.

2 Your Daily TRUSTED LEADER Intention
Pick one principle or value.

TODAY'S TL PRINCIPLE/VALUE:

PRINCIPLES
- ☐ Fear is the enemy of trust
- ☐ Really care
- ☐ People don't argue with what they help create
- ☐ There is collective wisdom in a team
- ☐ Refuse to be an adversary
- ☐ Set partnering ground rules
- ☐ To improve communication, stop talking and ask good questions
- ☐ Your success is determined by how you react to the challenges you face
- ☐ There is energy in conflict
- ☐ Understand all interests

VALUES
- ☐ Trust
- ☐ Fairness
- ☐ Transparency
- ☐ Respect
- ☐ Collaboration
- ☐ Helpfuless

MY TL INTENTION TODAY:

INNER VOICE FEEDBACK:

· ·

(3) **Plan for Using Your TRUSTED LEADER Intention**

I WILL INCORPORATE MY INTENTION INTO MY DAY AS FOLLOWS:

Everything can be taken from a man but one thing: to choose one's attitude in any given circumstance.
VIKTOR E. FRANKL

4 Observations

WHAT ARE YOU OBSERVING AS YOU IMPLEMENT YOUR INTENTION?

-
-
-
-
-
-
-
-
-
-

5 **Evening Ritual**

WHAT DID YOU LEARN TODAY?

☐ _____

☐ _____

☐ _____

☐ _____

☐ _____

6 **Repeat or Tweak?**

Look at your lessons learned, put an "X" next to those that did not work and a "*" next to those that did work (and that you want to repeat).

WEEKLY INSIGHTS

1 This Week's Insights

_____
_____
_____
_____
_____
_____
_____
_____

2 This Week's Lessons Learned

_____
_____
_____
_____
_____
_____
_____
_____

3 Things to Add to My Trusted Leader Arsenal

_____
_____
_____
_____
_____
_____

Notes

DAY56 | / /

1 Your Morning Ritual
Read/listen to your Trusted Leader Vision.

2 Your Daily TRUSTED LEADER Intention
Pick one principle or value.

TODAY'S TL PRINCIPLE/VALUE:		MY TL INTENTION TODAY:

PRINCIPLES

- ☐ Fear is the enemy of trust
- ☐ Really care
- ☐ People don't argue with what they help create
- ☐ There is collective wisdom in a team
- ☐ Refuse to be an adversary
- ☐ Set partnering ground rules
- ☐ To improve communica-tion, stop talking and ask good questions
- ☐ Your success is determined by how you react to the challenges you face
- ☐ There is energy in conflict
- ☐ Understand all interests

VALUES

- ☐ Trust
- ☐ Fairness
- ☐ Transparency
- ☐ Respect
- ☐ Collaboration
- ☐ Helpfuless

MY TL INTENTION TODAY:

_____

_____

_____

_____

_____

_____

_____

_____

INNER VOICE FEEDBACK:

_____

_____

_____

_____

_____

_____

_____

3 **Plan for Using Your TRUSTED LEADER Intention**

I WILL INCORPORATE MY INTENTION INTO MY DAY AS FOLLOWS:

The past does not equal the future.
ANTHONY ROBBINS

4 **Observations**

WHAT ARE YOU OBSERVING AS YOU IMPLEMENT YOUR INTENTION?

-
-
-
-
-
-
-
-
-
-

5 Evening Ritual

WHAT DID YOU LEARN TODAY?

☐

☐

☐

☐

☐

6 Repeat or Tweak?

Look at your lessons learned, put an "X" next to those that did not work and a "*" next to those that did work (and that you want to repeat).

DAY57 | / /

1 Your Morning Ritual
Read/listen to your Trusted Leader Vision.

2 Your Daily TRUSTED LEADER Intention
Pick one principle or value.

TODAY'S TL PRINCIPLE/VALUE:

PRINCIPLES
- ☐ Fear is the enemy of trust
- ☐ Really care
- ☐ People don't argue with what they help create
- ☐ There is collective wisdom in a team
- ☐ Refuse to be an adversary
- ☐ Set partnering ground rules
- ☐ To improve communication, stop talking and ask good questions
- ☐ Your success is determined by how you react to the challenges you face
- ☐ There is energy in conflict
- ☐ Understand all interests

VALUES
- ☐ Trust
- ☐ Fairness
- ☐ Transparency
- ☐ Respect
- ☐ Collaboration
- ☐ Helpfuless

MY TL INTENTION TODAY:

INNER VOICE FEEDBACK:

3 **Plan for Using Your TRUSTED LEADER Intention**

I WILL INCORPORATE MY INTENTION INTO MY DAY AS FOLLOWS:

4 Observations

WHAT ARE YOU OBSERVING AS YOU IMPLEMENT YOUR INTENTION?

-
-
-
-
-
-
-
-
-
-

5 Evening Ritual

WHAT DID YOU LEARN TODAY?

☐

☐

☐

☐

☐

6 Repeat or Tweak?

Look at your lessons learned, put an "X" next to those that did not work and a "" next to those that did work (and that you want to repeat).*

DAY58 | / /

1 Your Morning Ritual
Read/listen to your Trusted Leader Vision.

2 Your Daily TRUSTED LEADER Intention
Pick one principle or value.

TODAY'S TL PRINCIPLE/VALUE:

PRINCIPLES
- ☐ Fear is the enemy of trust
- ☐ Really care
- ☐ People don't argue with what they help create
- ☐ There is collective wisdom in a team
- ☐ Refuse to be an adversary
- ☐ Set partnering ground rules
- ☐ To improve communica- tion, stop talking and ask good questions
- ☐ Your success is determined by how you react to the challenges you face
- ☐ There is energy in conflict
- ☐ Understand all interests

VALUES
- ☐ Trust
- ☐ Fairness
- ☐ Transparency
- ☐ Respect
- ☐ Collaboration
- ☐ Helpfuless

MY TL INTENTION TODAY:

INNER VOICE FEEDBACK:

3 Plan for Using Your **TRUSTED LEADER** Intention

I WILL INCORPORATE MY INTENTION INTO MY DAY AS FOLLOWS:

The past does not equal the future.
ANTHONY ROBBINS

4 **Observations**

WHAT ARE YOU OBSERVING AS YOU IMPLEMENT YOUR INTENTION?

-

-

-

-

-

-

-

-

-

-

5 Evening Ritual

WHAT DID YOU LEARN TODAY?

☐

☐

☐

☐

☐

6 Repeat or Tweak?

*Look at your lessons learned, put an "X" next to those that did not work
and a "*" next to those that did work (and that you want to repeat).*

DAY59 | / /

1 Your Morning Ritual

Read/listen to your Trusted Leader Vision.

2 Your Daily TRUSTED LEADER Intention

Pick one principle or value.

TODAY'S TL PRINCIPLE/VALUE:

MY TL INTENTION TODAY:

PRINCIPLES

- ☐ Fear is the enemy of trust
- ☐ Really care
- ☐ People don't argue with what they help create
- ☐ There is collective wisdom in a team
- ☐ Refuse to be an adversary
- ☐ Set partnering ground rules
- ☐ To improve communication, stop talking and ask good questions
- ☐ Your success is determined by how you react to the challenges you face
- ☐ There is energy in conflict
- ☐ Understand all interests

VALUES

- ☐ Trust
- ☐ Fairness
- ☐ Transparency
- ☐ Respect
- ☐ Collaboration
- ☐ Helpfuless

INNER VOICE FEEDBACK:

3 **Plan for Using Your TRUSTED LEADER Intention**

I WILL INCORPORATE MY INTENTION INTO MY DAY AS FOLLOWS:

The past does not equal the future.
ANTHONY ROBBINS

4 **Observations**

WHAT ARE YOU OBSERVING AS YOU IMPLEMENT YOUR INTENTION?

-
-
-
-
-
-
-
-
-
-

5 **Evening Ritual**

WHAT DID YOU LEARN TODAY?

☐ _____

☐ _____

☐ _____

☐ _____

☐ _____

6 **Repeat or Tweak?**

Look at your lessons learned, put an "X" next to those that did not work and a "*" next to those that did work (and that you want to repeat).

DAY60 | / /

1 **Your Morning Ritual**
Read/listen to your Trusted Leader Vision.

2 **Your Daily TRUSTED LEADER Intention**
Pick one principle or value.

TODAY'S TL PRINCIPLE/VALUE:

PRINCIPLES
- ☐ Fear is the enemy of trust
- ☐ Really care
- ☐ People don't argue with what they help create
- ☐ There is collective wisdom in a team
- ☐ Refuse to be an adversary
- ☐ Set partnering ground rules
- ☐ To improve communica- tion, stop talking and ask good questions
- ☐ Your success is determined by how you react to the challenges you face
- ☐ There is energy in conflict
- ☐ Understand all interests

VALUES
- ☐ Trust
- ☐ Fairness
- ☐ Transparency
- ☐ Respect
- ☐ Collaboration
- ☐ Helpfuless

MY TL INTENTION TODAY:

INNER VOICE FEEDBACK:

3 Plan for Using Your **TRUSTED LEADER** Intention

I WILL INCORPORATE MY INTENTION INTO MY DAY AS FOLLOWS:

The past does not equal the future.
ANTHONY ROBBINS

❹ Observations

WHAT ARE YOU OBSERVING AS YOU IMPLEMENT YOUR INTENTION?

-

-

-

-

-

-

-

-

-

-

5 Evening Ritual

WHAT DID YOU LEARN TODAY?

☐

☐

☐

☐

☐

6 Repeat or Tweak?

Look at your lessons learned, put an "X" next to those that did not work and a "*" next to those that did work (and that you want to repeat).

WEEKLY **INSIGHTS**

1 This Week's Insights

_____
_____
_____
_____
_____
_____
_____
_____

2 This Week's Lessons Learned

_____
_____
_____
_____
_____
_____
_____
_____

3 Things to Add to My Trusted Leader Arsenal

_____
_____
_____
_____
_____
_____
_____

Notes

YOUR TRUSTED LEADER ARSENAL

In Practice Six you identified the things that really worked for you. Write them down in this section of your journal so you can remember them and refer back to them.

YOUR **TRUSTED LEADER** ARSENAL (CONTINUED)

YOUR **TRUSTED LEADER** ARSENAL (CONTINUED)

YOUR **TRUSTED LEADER** ARSENAL (CONTINUED)

TRUSTED LEADER RESOURCES

**We are here to help you along
your Trusted Leadership journey.
Check out our resources at:**
SUDYCO.COM/RESOURCES

Use the Partnering Approach to Become *the* Trusted Leader People Want to Follow

Imagine your business consistently producing extraordinary results that you, your team, and your customers, are excited about. Think what would be possible if you and your business were the most sought after in your market segment, and the best and brightest people wanted to work for you.

If you knew you could transform your business into a high performing team, that often does what others believe is impossible; through changing how you lead your business. Would you do it? Would you be intrigued?

The path to trusted leadership is a journey where you learn to drive out fear and develop a high trust atmosphere, so you can access the collective wisdom of your entire team, and customers. This path is put before you in eye-opening clarity by Sue Dyer's much anticipated new book. *The Trusted Leader: Use the Partnering Approach to Become the Trusted Leader People Want to Follow* reveals proven trusted leadership strategies that show you exactly how to:

- ▶ Think and Act like a Trusted Leader
- ▶ Drive out Fear with Trust
- ▶ Understand Your Personal Leadership Style and Trust Level
- ▶ Use the Partnering Principles and Mindset
- ▶ Grow a Culture of Trust
- ▶ Reap the Rewards of a High Trust High Performing Business

In addition, you will be able to create trusted leaders at all levels of your business so you can see even bigger results. Sue illustrates the trusted leader mindset with her many real-world cases where leaders have taken the partnering approach to become trusted leaders even in the most difficult of circumstances.

Connect with Sue

🌐 sudyco.com
✉ info@sudyco.com
in linkedin.com/in/suedyer

Take the sudyco™
Trusted Leader Profile

Sue Dyer developed the Trusted Leader Profile so you can better understand your leadership style and have a clear direction on where you need to go to increase trust in your business. After you've taken the free Trusted Leader Profile you will know:

▸ Where you fall along the sudyco™ Leadership Continuum

▸ How to understand your "normal leadership style" and your "perceived" leadership style"

▸ See if there is a gap between the norms you are setting and those you want in your business

▸ How to improve the level of trust you create in your business

SUDYCO.COM/PROFILE

It is recommended that you take the Trusted Leader Profile quarterly so you can see your progress!

sudyco™ CLASSES

Join Sue Dyer as you discover more about your personal leadership style and how trust is the essential ingredient in every successful business.

The Trusted Leader CLASS

Each free class shows you how:

- ▶ There is a continuum of leadership
- ▶ Understand your personal leadership style and its impact
- ▶ Unseen fear makes it impossible for you to lead
- ▶ Trust is the defining ingredient in your business
- ▶ Trusted Leadership is a rewarding journey

Apply today to learn more about mastering Trusted Leadership!

SUDYCO.COM/CLASS

The Trusted Leader MASTERCLASS

A guided tour on how to become a trusted leader using the proven Partnering Approach:

- ▶ Learn why trust is the essential ingredient for all businesses in the digital age
- ▶ Spot and drive out fear before it can undermine your business
- ▶ Discover your personal leadership style and how it impacts your business
- ▶ Unpack how culture determines your results and YOU set the culture

- ▶ Use the 10 Partnering Principles to create your leadership intentions
- ▶ Create a trusted leader mindset using the 6 Partnering Values
- ▶ Learn to train your brain so you can fully implement the Partnering Approach
- ★ **Get the equivalent of a master's degree in Trusted Leadership in one day!**

SUDYCO.COM/MASTERCLASS

THE sudyco™

Trusted Leadership Course

Imagine having lifetime access to Sue Dyer as your personal coach to walk you through how to become the trusted leader for your business by using the Partnering Approach to build a high trust high performing business.

The Trusted Leader Course is your step-by-step guide to:

- ▶ Developing a trusted leader mindset using the 6 Partnering Values
- ▶ Training your brain so you can fully implement the Partnering Approach
- ▶ Spotting and driving out fear before it can undermine your business results
- ▶ Discovering your personal leadership style and how it impacts your business
- ▶ Stop wasting of time and money when priorities are crossed
- ▶ Using the 10 Partnering Principles to create your leadership intentions

BUILD YOUR BUSINESS ON A FOUNDATION OF TRUST AND SOAR

Start building the high trust business you want today!
AT SUDYCO.COM/COURSE

sudyco™

Bring Sue, "the Godmother of Partering" and her team, into your business to help you create a Trust Strategy and Plan to take your business to the next level!

Trusted Leader MASTERMIND

The Trusted Leader Mastermind Includes:

- ▶ Become the trusted leader for your business using the Partnering Approach
- ▶ Find the best methods to achieve your business goals
- ▶ Get tools and resources to help you build and spread a culture of trust
- ▶ Shorten your learning curve by accessing the collective wisdom of other leaders

- ▶ Watch Sue deconstruct the steps to working through barriers and problems
- ▶ Increase your Trust Score
- ▶ Do the impossible by achieving what would not be possible today
- ▶ Network and connect with other Trusted Leaders

Begin your Trusted Leader journey today!

SUDYCO.COM/MASTERMIND

Trusted Leader CONSULTING

Trusted Leader Consulting Services Include:

- ▶ Trust Gap Analysis and Recommendations for your business
- ▶ Trust Strategy Development
- ▶ *Trust Blueprint* Facilitation with your Execution Team(s)
- ▶ *Trusted Leader Scorecard* with proprietary *Trusted Leader Momentum Score*
- ▶ Trust Steering Committee Development & Facilitation

Apply today to take your business to the next level!

SUDYCO.COM/CONSULTING

BRING THE sudyco™
The Trusted Leader
PRIVATE WORKSHOP
TO YOUR BUSINESS

Bring a sudyco™ certified facilitator to your business and learn how to apply the Partnering Approach directly to your business and create your 12-month trust plan.

AM The morning focuses on each person, as a leader, and works to improve their ability to lead. You will understand what kills businesses and how to overcome these forces. You will learn the sudyco™ Trusted Leader model and where you fall along the Continuum of Leadership. You will understand your strengths and weaknesses. Then you will learn the 2- keys to the Partnering Approach. So, you can start training your brain through daily practice to think and act like a Trusted Leader.

PM The afternoon focuses on implementing Trusted Leadership within your business so you achieve specific measurable results over the next year. You will evaluate the strengths and weaknesses of your current business culture, and where you can achieve the greatest benefit from improving the level of trust. Then you, and your leadership team, will co-create a 12-month Trusted Leader Implementation Plan specific for your business.

Book your private workshop
AT SUDYCO.COM/WORKSHOP

Take Sue's wisdom with you in your pocket, car, walk or office. Each week Sue and her guests bring to you the latest tips and strategies for becoming the trusted leader for your business—no matter where you are in your trusted leader journey.

Meet interesting guests who share their secrets and struggles as they journey to become trusted leaders for their businesses and hear from experts who will mentor you to leverage what you are doing for even better results.

▶ Get fired up to start a trust movement within your business

▶ Understand how trusted leaders think and act

▶ Learn how to create a high trust business atmosphere

▶ Discover what is possible with a high trust business culture

▶ Be mentored by those who know how to build a high trust, high performing team and business

SUE DYER, MBA, MIPI has helped more than 48,000 executive leaders to create high-trust business cultures over the past 35 years. She has been called the "godmother of partnering." Sue worked on over 4,000 projects worth over $180 billion to perfect her Partnering Approach model. She is the president of sudyco™ LLC, and the author of three other books, *Partner Your Project*, *Working Together*, and *On-Time On-Budget*. She lives in the San Francisco Bay area with her husband Bruce, and her grandson Noah. Her daughter Jennifer is disabled and loves reading and cooking. Her son Marc, and daughter-in-law Liz, are both physicians and are very active. They have two thriving sons, Owen and Kellen.

CPSIA information can be obtained
at www.ICGtesting.com
Printed in the USA
BVHW010437290122
627174BV00004B/78